Harold Nelson

Exercise Booklet

Simon & Schuster

Quick Access

REFERENCE FOR WRITERS

Fourth Edition

Lynn Quitman Troyka

PEARSON
Prentice
Hall

Upper Saddle River, New Jersey 07458

© 2004 by Pearson Education, Inc.
Upper Saddle River, New Jersey 07458

10 9 8 7 6 5 4 3 2 1

ISBN 0-13-182906-8
Printed in the United States of America

PREFACE FOR INSTRUCTORS

Many of us who use Lynn Quitman Troyka's *Quick Access Reference for Writers*, Fourth Edition, in our classes probably need exercises for quizzes, tests, homework, individualized instruction, supplementary material in a writing lab, questions for contests during class sessions, transparencies on which we demonstrate how to solve specific problems, or as training material for peer tutors. Having the exercises already written saves us preparation time.

This booklet meets the need. It contains sets of supplementary exercises for nine sections of *Quick Access*: Writing Process, Sentences, Words, Research, MLA Documentation, APA Documentation, Grammar Basics, Tips for Multilingual Writers, and Punctuation and Mechanics.

Each set contains fifteen exercises. The first five exercises in each set are lettered, and the next ten are numbered. Answers for the lettered exercises start on page 82 in this booklet. Answers for numbered exercises are in a separate *Answer Key* available to you through Prentice Hall.

Students can buy this *Exercise Booklet* at minimal cost. Or, if you prefer, please reprint, photocopy, or make transparencies from the booklet for use in classes in which you use *Quick Access*.

> Harold Nelson
> Minot State University
> Minot, North Dakota

PREFACE FOR STUDENTS

Lynn Troyka writes about the power and freedom that knowledge gives each of us: "Students are empowered by knowledge, for it frees us all to enjoy the pleasures of language and to fulfill, with energy and joy, our potentials as writers." I agree.

I have kept this idea in mind while writing this *Exercise Booklet*. I want the booklet to help you master the information in *Quick Access* in Sentences, Words, Grammar Basics, Tips for Multilingual Writers, and Punctuation and Mechanics. By increasing your knowledge in this way, you will grow in the freedom, power, and joy you feel when you write.

This booklet contains sets of exercises for specific sections in *Quick Access*. Each set contains five lettered exercises—with answers at the back of this booklet—and ten numbered exercises. Your instructor can order an *Answer Key* with answers to the numbered exercises.

You will learn best if you review the appropriate section(s) immediately before you do a set of exercises. Keep in mind the ideas you have just read as you complete the exercises.

When I was a boy, my father would tell me that "practice makes perfect." I have since learned that practice does not necessarily make perfect but that it does make better. The practice you do in this book should help you grow as a writer.

Harold Nelson
Minot State University
Minot, North Dakota

CONTENTS

TIPS FOR MULTILINGUAL WRITERS

PUNCTUATION

MECHANICS

Writing Processes: 10f—Avoiding Logical Fallacies

Identify the type of logical fallacy, if any, in each of the following sentences.

a. If we allow even one more member into the club, then we'll never stop the flow of new members and membership will become meaningless.

b. I'd rather take the train than the bus because, now that the train has been painted bright red with racing stripes, it looks so cool and streamlined.

c. Here's the star pitcher of our championship baseball team to tell you why you should look for your next car at Stadium Auto Sales.

d. Who would you prefer to run our town: Raul Banderson and his gang of beady-eyed accountants or Ron Sanders and his team of successful entrepreneurs?

e. Officer, I didn't run my car into that lamppost; suddenly the lamppost was right there in front of me and I couldn't stop in time.

1. All orange cats are especially mean and tough.

2. Everyone I know is voting for Jacquie over Michael for class president, so why don't you vote for Jacquie too?

3. Mr. Chamberlin simply cannot say he's a friend of the environment when we know he doesn't even do his own gardening; he hires a gardening service.

4. I wore my heavy jacket today, so of course it's the hottest day of the year.

5. Before we vote to fund the Science Building expansion, we ought to compare the plans for this new expansion with the work done on the same building two years ago.

6. I'm against Jane Smathers for Town Councilwoman: as a vegetarian she cannot be trusted.

7. This country needs either a complete, well-financed space program or no space program at all.

8. If you can raise your own vegetables, you can certainly cook us a wonderful meal.

9. I don't care how congested or dangerous that intersection has become, we have never had a traffic light there and I don't see any reason to have one now.

10. He's the tallest, so he must have the deepest voice.

SENTENCES: 15—Conciseness

Revise the following sentences for conciseness if necessary.

EXAMPLE:

The jacket is red. ~~in color.~~
                   ^

  a. As a matter of fact, I liked the movie.
  b. The ambulance driver made a decision to ignore the red light.
  c. There are fifteen different sandwiches listed on the menu.
  d. John, who is a good athlete, wants to play professional football.
  e. The bill that was introduced into the House was introduced by the Speaker.

1. The point I am trying to make is that this potato salad needs more salt.
2. As a matter of fact, in the case of this year's school band, nearly every school band member is an accomplished musician.
3. For the purpose of saving energy, everyone in our office turns the lights off when they leave a room they had been using.
4. Mr. Jones, who is my neighbor, lives in my neighborhood.
5. Your completion of the paper several days before it is due will result in an opportunity for your relaxation immediately before handing in the paper.
6. There are five different meal plans offered by the food service.
7. Due to the fact that one can now conduct a search on the Internet, it is easier than ever before to find information on most subjects.
8. James Butler Hickok was born in 1837 and died in 1876, and he worked as a frontier scout and as a marshal, and he is known as "Wild Bill" Hickok.
9. Shopping for antiques, which is a serious pastime for some people, can get to be a costly hobby.
10. The professor's suggestion to Jane is that she increase her motivation if she wants to pass the course successfully.

SENTENCES: 15—Conciseness

Revise the following sentences for conciseness if necessary.

EXAMPLE:

The car was dirty, rusty, and ~~it had been manufactured many years ago.~~ old.

a. The house was large, old, and it had drafts.
b. With the endlessly conflicting reports of research studies on healthy dietary habits, first saying one thing about what we should eat then saying the exact opposite thing, it's difficult to know what we should be eating.
c. The bottom line is the line that shows profit or loss.
d. People often extend this literal meaning of bottom line, and they use the phrase to mean the determining consideration in a decision.
e. Our next door neighbor couldn't get his car started yesterday, so he had it towed to his mechanic, whom he trusts to fix it properly.

1. The cat is large, gray and it likes people.
2. The cat, which belongs to my sister, who is older than I am, sleeps at least eighteen hours every day.
3. I like the cat that my sister has.
4. My sister has a cat, but I have a dog instead of a cat.
5. My sister likes my dog, and my sister generally likes animals.
6. The 2000 election for president of the United States was one of the most highly contested of all the elections for president in the history of the U.S.
7. Albert Gore and George W. Bush each conducted long and hard campaigns, each focusing his campaign on his strongest supporters, and each attempting to act like what most people think a president should act like.
8. As it turned out, nearly everyone was taken by surprise because, by the end of Election Day, we still did not know who was elected president on that Election Day.
9. Although Albert Gore received more popular votes nationwide than George W. Bush, the Electoral College vote was tied, with Florida not yet decided due to ballot count disputes and voting recounts.
10. In the final analysis, the election was decided in Bush's favor when the U.S. Supreme Court ended five weeks of voting recount efforts in Florida when the tally had Bush ahead by 537 votes.

SENTENCES: 16a–b—Coordination

Combine the following sentences to illustrate coordination. Do not show coordination in the same way in two successive sentences. Add or delete words or punctuation marks, but do no major rewriting.

EXAMPLE:

The sky became dark. The moon rose.
The sky became dark, and the moon rose.

a. The French Revolution began in 1789. It ended France's thousand-year monarchy.
b. King Louis XVI assembled the French Parliament to deal with France's huge debt. The common people's part of Parliament proclaimed itself France's true legislature.
c. King Louis protested. A crowd destroyed the royal prison.
d. A constitutional monarchy was established. Some people thought the king would be content.
e. King Louis and the queen, Marie Antoinette, tried to leave the country. They were caught, convicted of treason, and executed.

1. In the Pacific Northwest, clams are *steamers*. In New England, clams are *quahogs*.
2. Littleneck clams are small. They are the tenderest East Coast hardshells.
3. Surf clams are West Coast hardshells. They are larger and tougher than littlenecks.
4. Littlenecks are normally steamed. Surf clams are normally minced for chowder or cut into strips for frying.
5. The East Coast provides most of the commercial clams caught in the United States. The West Coast provides fewer and less common varieties.
6. Today is Samantha's birthday. She won't tell anybody her age.
7. An orthodontist applies gentle and gradual pressure on the patient's teeth. This guides them into the proper position.
8. Mr. Farhood uses his cell phone for all of his nonlocal calls. This greatly reduces his long-distance phone bill.
9. My cousin's pie crust is the best I've ever tasted. It is tender, flaky, and flavored perfectly.
10. Michael is at his computer doing instant messaging all night long. He still gets his studying done.

4

SENTENCES: 16c–d—Subordination

Combine the following sentences to illustrate subordination. Do not show subordination in the same way in two successive sentences. Add or delete words or punctuation marks, but do no major rewriting. For items a–e, the event in the first sentence occurred before the event in the second.

EXAMPLE:

The sky became dark. The moon rose.
After the sky became dark, the moon rose.

a. The French Revolution began in 1789. It ended France's thousand-year monarchy.
b. King Louis XVI assembled the French Parliament to deal with France's huge debt. The common people's part of Parliament proclaimed itself France's true legislature.
c. King Louis protested. A crowd destroyed the royal prison.
d. A constitutional monarchy was established. Some people thought the king would be content.
e. King Louis and the queen, Marie Antoinette, tried to leave the country. They were caught, convicted of treason, and executed.

1. In the Pacific Northwest, clams are *steamers*. In New England, clams are *quahogs*.
2. Littleneck clams are small. They are the tenderest East Coast hardshells.
3. Surf clams are West Coast hardshells. They are larger and tougher than littlenecks.
4. Littlenecks are normally steamed. Surf clams are normally minced for chowder or cut into strips for frying.
5. The East Coast provides most of the commercial clams caught in the United States. The West Coast provides fewer and less common varieties.
6. Jennie had a mild cold yesterday. All she had to eat was tea and toast.
7. The planetarium's trip to see the solar eclipse has left. I decided too late that I wanted to go after all.
8. Sometimes you can improve a photograph outdoors by using a flash attachment. I brought along my flash attachment.
9. The kayak club accepts anyone who has experience with kayaks. Wanda and Randy joined that club.
10. Ms. Lenahan has a specific idea of luxury in her office. It is having an automatic letter opener and automatic stapler.

SENTENCES: 17a—Parallelism

Revise any sentences showing faulty parallelism.

EXAMPLE:

attending
Professor Smith recommends studying the text and ~~to attend~~ class.

a. Archimedes was an ancient Greek scientist, mathematician, and he made inventions.
b. According to legend, Archimedes is supposed to have said both "Give me the place to stand and a lever long enough, and I will move the earth" and to have shouted "Eureka!" when he stepped into his bath and realized that he could measure the volume of an object by determining the volume of the water it displaces when submerged.
c. Archimedes discovered the principle of buoyancy, he discovered formulas for calculating the areas of various geometric figures, and he is remembered as the inventor of the Archimidean screw.
d. According to the principle of buoyancy, a boat floats and balloons will rise because they weigh less than the water or air they displace.
e. Math students will study the formulas Archimedes discovered in geometry, and engineering students still study his ideas about applying geometry to hydrostatics and mechanics.

1. I want to stop feeling lethargic, irritable, and looking unattractive.
2. My doctor recommends that I lose ten pounds, exercise each day, and to sleep at least seven hours each night.
3. I'll follow my doctor's advice because I want to look better and because I want to be feeling better.
4. It's surprising how much neglecting the body's needs can affect both our physical well-being and mental outlook.
5. I'm going to be joining a health club, I'm going to be going on a diet, and I'm going to be following my doctor's advice.
6. I start each session with leg stretching, back bends, and sit-ups.
7. My exercise consists of both taking long runs and of walking whenever I can.
8. It's difficult for most of us to set aside the time to exercise, avoiding other tempting pursuits, and changing our sedentary habits.
9. Those who expect immediate results from exercise are going to be disappointed or they will be angry.
10. I took years to reach this condition, so I expect it will take months to change the condition significantly.

Follow the directions in parentheses after each of the following sentences.

EXAMPLE:

An acid is a sour-tasting substance. Lemon juice is an acid. Acid often dissolves other materials. (Combine into one sentence.)

An acid, such as lemon juice, is a sour-tasting substance that often dissolves other materials.

    a. My friend Barbara has a "hybrid" car that runs on both gasoline and electricity, and it charges its battery whenever she uses the brakes. (Rewrite as two sentences.)
    b. The man walked. (Add an adjective.)
    c. The man walked. (Add an adverb.)
    d. The man walked. (Add an adverb clause.)
    e. The man walked. (Add an adjective clause.)

1. Hemophilia is an inherited disease. It is caused by a deficiency or abnormality of one of the clotting factors. These factors are in the blood. Hemophiliacs can bleed to death from even small cuts or bruises. (Combine into one sentence.)
2. The dog jumped into the pond. (Invert the word order by placing the verb before the subject.)
3. The wind blew. (Add an adjective.)
4. The wind blew. (Add an adverb.)
5. The wind blew. (Add a prepositional phrase.)
6. The wind blew. (Add a participial phrase.)
7. The wind blew. (Add an absolute phrase.)
8. The wind blew. (Add an adverb phrase.)
9. The wind blew. (Add an adverb clause.)
10. The wind blew. (Add an adjective clause.)

SENTENCES: 11—Sentence Fragments

Revise the following, if necessary, to eliminate any fragments.

EXAMPLE:

Albert Schweitzer, the German theologian, musician, and physician, received many awards for his work as a humanitarian and missionary in Africa. Including the Nobel Peace Prize.

Albert Schweitzer, the German theologian, musician, and physician, received many awards, including the Nobel Peace Prize, for his work as a humanitarian and missionary in Africa.

a. What is the difference between a cat and a sentence? A cat has claws at the end of its paws, and a sentence has a pause at the end of its clause.
b. Today, *girl* denotes a female child. In Middle English, *girl* is a child of either sex.
c. The word *balkanization* derives from the name of the Balkan Peninsula, which was divided into several small nations. In the early twentieth century.
d. Bacteria, at times present in incorrectly canned or preserved foods, causes botulism, a type of food poisoning. Which is often fatal if not treated properly.
e. Many people use hand cream because their skin gets too dry. During the winter.

1. A big dark ring of sesame-covered Turkish bread. Called *simit*.
2. Turkish salads contain vegetables that Americans associate with Italy. They also often contain ingredients that Americans associate with countries east of Turkey.
3. A dozen words for *peat*. In the Irish language.
4. Snow hardens into glaciers. Which cover roughly ten percent of the earth's land.
5. On my birthday. All I want is to take the day completely off. Nothing to do.
6. Computers become important appliances. Most people only got their computers within the last ten years.
7. Just about everyone. Has one now, but the VCR was once an amazing luxury.
8. Perhaps within ten years, everyone will have a satellite positioning device. Always know our exact latitude and longitude.
9. In the early seventeenth century. Henry Hudson explored the Hudson River.
10. In computer science, a bit is the smallest unit of information. A blend of b(inary) and (dig)it.

SENTENCES: 12—Comma Splices and Run-on Sentences

Revise the following sentences to eliminate comma splices and run-on sentences.

EXAMPLE:

and
I bought the tickets, we attended the concert.
                    ∧

a. These days, a significant proportion of camera-buyers are opting for digital rather than conventional cameras the cost of digital cameras has come down and the quality of their photos is steadily increasing.

b. Part of the purchase decision depends on determining whether the quality of digital photos is high enough photo quality depends on the photographer's taste and on what use to which the photos will be put.

c. For example, many people just want snapshots of their friends and family this type of photography does not require an expensive, highly sophisticated digital camera.

d. Others, including serious amateur photographers, want their photos to have the highest resolution and color accuracy that is possible.

e. As in most things, the greater the capability of the digital camera, the more expensive it is Fortunately, there is a wide range of capabilities from which to choose.

1. Some people frown on gambling, many phrases in American English originally were associated with gambling.

2. President Harry Truman kept a sign on his desk that said "The buck stops here," the phrase was originally used in poker games in the 1800s.

3. The dealer in the poker game passed a knife with a handle made of buck horn to another player, that person became the new dealer.

4. *Passing the buck* had a literal origin it meant passing the knife (and the deal).

5. White, red, and blue chips are used for betting in poker, with blue chips being the most valuable, similarly, blue-chip stocks on the stock market are normally the most stable, secure, and valuable.

6. Italian cheeses come in a variety of types, not all are hard cheeses for grating.

7. Italian mozzarella is made from water-buffalo milk it has a short shelf life so it is unlike the mozzarella Americans put on pizzas.

8. Fontina is a mild and relatively soft cheese which is suitable for slicing or spreading, aged provolone is a sharp and hard cheese which is suitable for grating.

9. Fontina that is produced high in the Alps in the summer has a higher fat content than ordinary fontina, this extra fat makes the summer fontina highly prized.

10. Mozzarella made of water-buffalo milk has a shelf life of several days, provolone may be aged two years before it is ready.

SENTENCES: 13—Shifting and Disjointed Sentences

Revise the following sentences if necessary.

EXAMPLE:

                people visit
When a̶ ̶p̶e̶r̶s̶o̶n̶ ̶v̶i̶s̶i̶t̶s̶ Yellowstone Park, they should do a lot of walking.

  a. I enjoy reading my horoscope, but you really wonder if it's ever true.
  b. Keeping fit may not help you live longer, but it will make your later years more comfortable. You should exercise regularly.
  c. By standing inside the penalty area allows a soccer goalie to handle the ball.
  d. My cousin Shawn, who is 35 years old, never learned riding a bicycle.
  e. The reason I am emphasizing that you be more punctual is because you have missed your train four days in a row.

1. A private citizen may legally make an arrest if they have observed a crime or have reasonable cause to believe a crime has been committed.
2. The more a person studies a foreign language, the better they should expect to speak it.
3. Many students expect to find jobs in their major fields eventually, but some problems are probably anticipated.
4. The majority of the students in my political science class identified three main goals for government: balance the budget, reduce crime, and protect the environment.
5. By working out makes an individual physically fit.
6. Friday was when the computer technician came to my office to replace my defective CD drive.
7. The purpose of the George Washington Bridge was built to span the Hudson River.
8. The reason for the increase in club dues was instituted to pay for an extension to the clubhouse.
9. Canada is where there is the most coastline in a country.
10. Some people think that space colonies will eventually relieve crowding on earth, but that possibility is doubted by me.

SENTENCES: 14—Misplaced and Dangling Modifiers

Revise misplaced and dangling modifiers in the following sentences if necessary.

EXAMPLE:

completely
How the police officer subdued the violent suspect ~~completely~~ amazed
me.
                         ^

  a. The members of the hiking group made their gradually way to the trailhead.

  b. The hike leader quickly explained where they would be going, eager to get started.

  c. Three hikers said that this, expressing their concern, was their first hike ever.

  d. An experienced hiker took the position of "sweep," which meant she would go last to make sure nobody got stranded.

  e. The tired but exhilarated, seven hours later, group completed the challenging hike and celebrated at a local restaurant.

  1. Stolen from our room last week, my roommate saw our stereo equipment in the pawn shop.

  2. My roommate saw our stereo equipment in the pawn shop that was stolen from our room last week.

  3. We immediately called the police.

  4. Two officers arrived and talked with the owner of the pawn shop, determined to solve the crime.

  5. The officers wanted to quickly solve the crime.

  6. In talking with the owner of the pawn shop, it seemed her nephew was the most likely suspect.

  7. Unwilling to believe that her nephew had stolen the stereo, a mistake was the explanation the owner of the pawn shop gave.

  8. My roommate and I told the officers that we only knew her nephew slightly but that we had not given him our stereo equipment.

  9. Engraved on each piece of equipment, the officers spotted our Social Security numbers, which proved that the equipment was ours.

10. After his sentencing, the nephew was sure by January that he would be on parole.

WORDS: 19b—Choosing Exact Words

The first three lettered sentences and first five numbered sentences contain inappropriate denotations or connotations. The other sentences contain general or abstract phrases. Revise accordingly.

EXAMPLES:

famous.
Mahatma Gandhi is ~~notorious~~. (denotation / connotation)

at 3:45 p.m.
Meet me ~~this afternoon~~. (general / abstract)

a. The gardener's hide was sunburned. (denotation/connotation)
b. The basketball player is lofty. (denotation/connotation)
c. Her perfume has a wonderful odor. (denotation/connotation)
d. I bought a vehicle. (general/abstract)
e. Janet's house is a long way from here. (general/abstract)

1. The customer politely demanded that I help her. (denotation/connotation)
2. I buy my groceries at the boutique. (denotation/connotation)
3. The professor commended us that we'd have a quiz soon. (denotation/connotation)
4. I clandestinely hid the present. (denotation/connotation)
5. We want to commemorate you for a job well done. (denotation/connotation)
6. I read the book. (general/abstract)
7. On our trip, we went to many different places. (general/abstract)
8. I want to complete my education. (general/abstract)
9. You should make your presentation shorter. (general/abstract)
10. Your watch is not set correctly. (general/abstract)

WORDS: 19d—Using Appropriate Language

Revise words with inappropriate impact in the following sentences if necessary.

EXAMPLE:
prison.

My brother is in ~~a rehabilitation facility.~~

a. If you agree with Mr. Anderson's argument, then you're living in a dream world.
b. I think I'll flunk accounting.
c. Contemporaries often described the artist Vincent van Gogh as all ears.
d. The door wouldn't close because the carpenters had inserted it at variance with the instructions.
e. Nobody ever arrives early to the board meeting, so there's no need to rush.

1. We ain't done.
2. On the football field he is a bear in the forest, but at home he is a cream puff.
3. This car stops on a dime.
4. If I don't get a handle on these math problems, I'll be up the creek in math class.
5. The candidate misspoke herself.
6. He's happy as a lark and smart as a whip.
7. A person needs to be tough as nails to reach the top of the heap.
8. After all is said and done, far be it from me at this point in time to disagree.
9. With all these new responsibilities, I feel like I'm hauling an elephant on my back.
10. The coat your aunt gave you has seen better days.

WORDS: 20—Gender-Neutral Language

Revise sexist language in the following sentences.

EXAMPLE:

specialized
Operating a drill press is a ~~man-sized~~ job.

  a. Jane is the new chairman of our committee.
  b. The Constitution gives every American the right to speak his mind.
  c. The men in the room applauded.
  d. All policemen should be honest.
  e. Mike was a house husband: He cleaned, took care of the children, and cooked.

1. I always make sure the shopping clerk enters my purchases correctly on her cash register.
2. Whenever a new nurse comes to help you, be sure to treat her with respect.
3. When a driver is stopped for a traffic violation, she should be polite to the policeman.
4. Our mission is to go where no man has gone before.
5. All men should exercise regularly.
6. An elementary school teacher has her hands full, since she works with so many giggling girls and rowdy boys.
7. Women who want to become better cooks should read this magazine.
8. My aunt, who works as an accountant, is a career girl.
9. This candidacy needs a slogan with which all men can agree.
10. Men need to have extensive training before they can qualify to become pilots.

WORDS: 21—Spelling

Correct misspelled words in the following sentences.

EXAMPLE:

My two ~~sister-in-laws~~ <u>sisters-in-law</u> live in San Francisco.

a. Just remember that your now among friends.
b. Can your restaurant accomodate a dinner party of 26 people?
c. It is relatively easy to learn to drive, but driving well requires experance.
d. Alyssa has had her driver's lisence for two years now.
e. I'd like to order some stationary for my new business.

1. Tornadoes occur relatively frequently on the Great Planes in late spring and in the summer.
2. They are often accompanied by rain, hail, and lightening.
3. Tornadoes themselves affect relatively small areas; there normally ten yards to a mile wide.
4. The territory touched by a tornado is often raised.
5. People have seen tornadoes move army tanks, farm combines, and railroad cars.
6. As in the movie *The Wizard of Oz*, in which a tornado picks up Dorothy's house, tornadoes have moved hole houses.
7. A tornado is able to brake nearly anything in its path, since its winds reach 300 mph.
8. Most buildings are not tornado-proof, sense tornadoes carry such incredible energy.
9. During a few minutes, a thunderstorm that produces a tornado might let lose the same energy as a one-megaton atomic bomb.
10. When human structures and tornadoes meat, the tornadoes normally win.

WORDS: 21a—Spelling Plurals

Correct misspelled words in the following sentences.

EXAMPLE:

My brother and my sister are both ~~coachs.~~ coaches.

a. Carl prefers his french frys without ketchup.
b. He was at two beachs yesterday.
c. He wore a shirt with long sleeves, but he wore swim trunks.
d. He wore shoes, so his foots are fine.
e. Carl is one of my brother-in-laws.

1. Please get some baking potatos when you go shopping.
2. Do your datums support your conclusion?
3. In this folder, I keep the syllabi for all my classes.
4. At Valley Forge, you can see many deers grazing out in the open.
5. We saw a herd of elks when we were at the zoo.
6. Every morning, as soon as I wake up, I do 50 sit-upes.
7. Did you rake the leafs?
8. We visited four zooes while we were on vacation.
9. There are many phenomenons in our world for which we cannot account by rational explanations.
10. When we went camping in the northern wilderness, we saw a pack of wolf.

WORDS: 21b–c—Adding Suffixes and Spelling *ie, ei* words

Correct misspelled words in the following sentences.

EXAMPLE:

In my opinion, fast food will never ~~supercede~~ ^{supersede} home-cooked food.

a. The results of your survey are not statisticaly correct.
b. I beleive I will have my hair cut.
c. Did you paint the cieling?
d. When did they begin requiring a jacket and tie in the restaurant?
e. The company exseeded its sales goal for the year by the end of the first quarter.

1. The gas station attendant examined the money I gave him as though it were counterfiet.
2. My nieghbor bought it.
3. She will likly not ride it in the fields.
4. I find myself likeing to read more than I did when I was in high school.
5. I have a strong drive to succede.
6. My roommate droped his books on the desk.
7. Everyone arrived on time because you wrote the directions correctly.
8. Our family has gone two weeks without friing anything.
9. Did you take into account the cost of frieght?
10. That was a wierd movie.

WORDS: 21d—Spelling Homonyms

Correct misspelled words in the following sentences.

EXAMPLE:
    too
I ate ~~to~~ many potato chips.

a. This is a tough decision to make, so we're asking for your council.
b. I except the invitation.
c. We went to the state fare.
d. This schedule is all together confusing.
e. It is better to recycle paper than to waist it.

1. My mother is principle at an elementary school.
2. Who's hat is this?
3. Is it your hat?
4. Did you meat the visitors?
5. We past the car.
6. Your actions do not altar the harm of your statements.
7. It's been reigning for three hours.
8. Please devise a plan that divides the work fairly among everyone.
9. I would like to by the chair buy next week.
10. My favorite part of dinner is desert.

WORDS: 21d—Spelling Commonly Confused Words

Correct misspelled words in the following sentences.

EXAMPLE:

                    illusion.

The Wizard of Oz is a master of ~~allusion.~~

  a. You can always spot me from afar by the cloths I'm wearing.
  b. Cheese and milk are diary products.
  c. This is the quite before the storm.
  d. I can't discuss what Yusef told me because it's personnel.
  e. If you're ready to begin, you may precede.

  1. Where you in class on Tuesday?
  2. Please take the wrench off the car seat.
  3. Thank you for the birthday presence you gave me.
  4. I wish to respectively disagree.
  5. I prefer the later, rather than the former.
  6. The fable's morale is clear.
  7. We can't wait to see the zoo's new guerrilla exhibit.
  8. Did you chose wisely?
  9. This lever is a handy devise.
 10. It is my responsibility and my pleasure to formerly announce that Emily is our new president.

Read the following passage, then follow the instructions below.

Gates wrote his first software program at the age of 13. In high school he helped form a group of programmers who computerized their school's payroll system and founded Traf-O-Data, a company that sold traffic-counting systems to local governments. In 1975 Gates, then a sophomore at Harvard University, joined his hometown friend Paul G. Allen to develop software for the first microcomputers. They began by adapting BASIC, a popular programming language used on large computers, for use on microcomputers. With the success of this project, Gates left Harvard during his junior year and, with Allen, formed Microsoft. Gates's sway over the infant microcomputer industry greatly increased when Microsoft licensed an operating system called MS-DOS to International Business Machines Corporation—then the world's biggest computer supplier and industry pacesetter—for use on its first microcomputer, the IBM PC (personal computer). After the machine's release in 1981, IBM quickly set the technical standard for the PC industry, and MS-DOS likewise pushed out competing operating systems. While Microsoft's independence strained relations with IBM, Gates deftly manipulated the larger company so that it became permanently dependent on him for crucial software. Makers of IBM-compatible PCs, or clones, also turned to Microsoft for their basic software. By the start of the 1990s he had become the PC industry's ultimate kingmaker.

Largely on the strength of Microsoft's success, Gates amassed a huge paper fortune as the company's largest individual shareholder. He became a paper billionaire in 1986, and within a decade his net worth had reached into the tens of billions of dollars—making him by some estimates the world's richest private individual. With few interests beyond software and the potential of information technology, Gates at first preferred to stay out of the public eye, handling civic and philanthropic affairs indirectly through one of his foundations. Nevertheless, as Microsoft's power and reputation grew, and especially as it attracted the attention of the U.S. Justice Department's antitrust division, Gates, with some reluctance, became a more public figure. Rivals (particularly in competing companies in Silicon Valley) portrayed him as driven, duplicitous, and determined to profit from virtually every electronic transaction in the world. His supporters, on the other hand, celebrated his uncanny business acumen, his flexibility, and his boundless appetite for finding new ways to make computers and electronics more useful through software.

Source: "Gates, Bill." Encyclopedia Britannica. 2003 ed.

Research 26g—Avoiding Plagiarism

Revise the following sentences that paraphrase the above passage to eliminate the plagiarism.

a. Bill Gates wrote his first software program at the age of 13.
b. While in high school, Gates helped form a group of programmers who computerized their school's payroll system and founded Traf-O-Data, a company that sold traffic-counting systems to local governments.
c. In 1975, as a sophomore at Harvard University, Gates joined his hometown friend Paul G. Allen to develop software for the first microcomputers.
d. They adapted BASIC, a popular programming language used on large computers, for use on microcomputers.
e. This project was successful, so Gates left Harvard during his junior year and formed Microsoft with Allen.

1. When Microsoft licensed an operating system called MS-DOS to International Business Machines Corporation, Gates's sway over the infant microcomputer industry increased greatly.
2. After the first microcomputer, The IBM PC (personal computer) was released in 1981, IBM quickly set the technical standard for the PC industry, and MS-DOS likewise pushed out competing operating systems.
3. Although IBM was not happy with Microsoft's independence, Gates deftly manipulated the larger company so that it became permanently dependent on him for crucial software.
4. The manufacturers of clones, which were IBM-compatible PCs, also turned to Microsoft for their basic software.
5. In the early 1990s, Gates had become the PC industry's ultimate kingmaker.
6. Gates compiled a huge paper fortune as the company's largest individual shareholder, largely on the strength of Microsoft's success.
7. By 1986, he was a paper billionaire, and within ten years his net worth had reached into the tens of billions of dollars
8. This made him by some estimates the world's richest private individual.
9. However, as Microsoft's power and reputation attracted the attention of the U.S. Justice Department's antitrust division, Gates, with some reluctance, became a more public figure.
10. His rivals portrayed him as driven, duplicitous, and determined to profit from nearly every electronic transaction in the world, while his supporters focused on his uncanny business acumen, his flexibility, and his boundless appetite for finding new ways to make computers and electronics more useful through software.

Revise the following citations, if necessary, using MLA Guidelines
a. Cayton, Andrew; Perry, Elisabeth Israels; Reed, Linda; and Winkler, Allan M. America: Pathways to the Present. Upper Saddle River, NJ: Prentice Hall, 2003.
b. Goldman, Edwin Franko, and Walter M. Smith, ed. Arban's Complete Conservatory Method for Trumpet, New York: Carl Fischer, 1982.
c. Olver, Lynne, and Chipello, Christopher J. "British Columbia Acts to Inject Market Forces Into Lumber Prices." Wall Street Journal. 27 March 2003: A2.
d. "Inline Efficiency." Popular Science March 2003, 22.
e. King, Nelson. Add Organization to Outlook. PC Magazine 24 December 2002:48.

1. Greenman, Ben. "Nspace: Diary of a Cosmonaut." The New Yorker (4 November 2002): 48.
2. Perl, Philip. Ferns. Time-Life Encyclopedia of Gardening Ser., Alexandria, VA: Time-Life Books, 1977.
3. McClelland, Deke, Photoshop 6 for Windows Bible. New York: Hungry Minds, Inc., 2001.
4. "Amadeus." Screenplay by Peter Shaffer. Dir. Milos Forman. Prod. Saul Zaentz. Perf. F. Murray Abraham, Elizabeth Berridge, and Simon Callow, Videocassette.The Saul Zaentz Company, 1997.
5. Map of Nassau County, New York. Map. Maspeth, NY: Hagstrom (1997).
6. Lincoln, Abraham. "Second Inaugural Address." United States Capitol Building. Washington, D.C. 4 March 1865.
7. George Frideric Handel. "Handel's Messiah." Cond. Robert Shaw. Robert Shaw Chorale and Orchestra. RCA Victor, 1966.
   and Orchestra. RCA Victor, 1966.
8. Tanakh: The Holy Scriptures, Philadelphia: The Jewish Publication Society (1985).
9. Agel, Jerome. The Making of Kubrick's "2001." New York, Signet, 1970.
10. Brown, John Russell. Introduction. Henry V. By William Shakespeare. New York: Signet, 1965. xxiii-xxxviii.

Revise the following citations, if necessary, using APA Guidelines

a. Swartz. S. (1989, March 31). Why Michael Milken stands to qualify for Guinness Book. Wall Street Journal, 1.
b. Steele, R. June 2000. Awful but lawful. *Boating,* 36.
c. Pinker, S. (2002). *The blank slate,* New York: Penguin Putnam.
d. Goldstein, E. B. (1999). *Sensation and perception.* (5th ed.). Pacific Grove, CA: Brooks-Cole.
e. Greenfield, P.M. (1998). "The cultural evolution of IQ." In U. Neisser (Ed.), *The Rising Curve: Long-Term Gains in IQ and Related Measures* (pp. 81-123). Washington, DC: American Psychological Association.

1. Schneider, W. and Bjorklund, D. F. (1998). Memory. In W. Damon (Ed.), *Handbook of Child Psychology* (Vol. 2). New York: Wiley.
2. "Perception" (2003). In *Encyclopedia Britannica.*
3. *U.S. Department of Health and Human Services.* (1997) Vital statistics of the United States, 1994. Washington, DC: U.S. Government Printing Office.
4. Stunkard, A. J., Sorensen, T. I. A., Hanis, C., Teasdale, T. W., Chakraborty, R., Schull, W. J., & Schulsinger, F. (1986). An adoption study of human obesity. *New England Journal of Medicine,* 317. 830-831.
5. Edman, P., & W. V. Friesen, (1975). *Unmasking the Face.* Englewood Cliffs, NJ: Prentice Hall.
6. Rubin, K. H., Coplan, R. J., Chen, X., & McKinnon, J. E. (1994). Peer relationships and influences in childhood. In Ramachandran, V. S., (Ed.), *Encyclopedia of human behavior* (Vol. 3, pp. 431-439). San Diego, CA: Academic Press.
7. Barash, D. P. & Lipton, J. E. (2001), *The Myth of Monogomy.* New York: W. H. Freeman.
8. Whitman, D. 1989, March 20). Shattering myths about the homeless. *U.S. News & World Report,* 26, 28.
9. Caplow, T., Bahr, H. M., Modell, J., & Chadwick, B. A. (1991). Recent Social Trends in the United States, 1960-1990. *Montreal: McGill-Queen's University Press.*
10. Zigler, E. F., & Styfco, S. J. (1994). Head Start: Criticisms in a Constructive Context. *American Psychologist,* 49, 127-132.

GRAMMAR BASICS: 39j—Subjects and Verbs

Underline subjects once and verbs twice in the following sentences.

EXAMPLE:

Roberto ordered a soft drink.

a. The weather was delightfully mild yesterday.
b. Everyone went to the park to enjoy the day.
c. In fact, the park was too crowded.
d. We decided to make the best of it.
e. A quiet walk in the woods gave us some relief.

1. The members of the team were tired and happy.
2. They had played hard, and they had won.
3. Years of hard work had led to their success.
4. Frank and Susan ski well.
5. Frank and Susan enjoy skiing.
6. The dog chased the cat.
7. My neighbor owns both animals.
8. He normally keeps them apart.
9. Unfortunately, he forgot to shut the door to the house.
10. The dog and the cat ran into the house and knocked over two lamps.

GRAMMAR BASICS: 40a—Transitive and Intransitive Verbs

Underline transitive verbs once and intransitive verbs twice in the following sentences.

EXAMPLE:

Jane <u>talked</u> to Mark.

a. I saw Helena at the gym this morning.
b. Her workout was extremely strenuous.
c. Afterward, she limped back to the dressing room.
d. Maybe I was wrong, but I offered her some advice.
e. I told her to build up her strength before she tries another difficult workout.

1. Christopher Marlowe wrote the sixteenth-century English play *Doctor Faustus*.
2. In Goethe's *Faust*, Mephistopheles tempts Faust.
3. Faust sells his soul to the powers of darkness.
4. Charles Gounod's opera *Faust* is about the same story.
5. Gounod wrote his opera in 1859.
6. Susan B. Anthony worked for women's rights.
7. She was an active abolitionist (antislavery reformer) before the Civil War.
8. In 1869, she cofounded the National Woman Suffrage Association.
9. Anthony is particularly famous for her work in women's suffrage, or right to vote.
10. She died in 1920.

GRAMMAR BASICS: 40b—Regular and Irregular Verbs

Revise verbs in the following sentences if necessary.

EXAMPLE:

My shoes were ~~suppose~~ ^{supposed} to be polished.

a. I dived off the high board.
b. Have you ever dove off the high board?
c. The water in the pool were cold today.
d. Until recently, I would have sank in water over my head.
e. I have grew stronger as a swimmer in recent weeks.

1. At last night's election for club officers, I run for president.
2. It looked like everybody taked my speech seriously.
3. I hoped that everyone who knowed me would vote for me.
4. I won, but I was keeped that the other candidates had to lose.
5. Ron be studying for the test in economics class.
6. He sworn last week that he would get a good grade in the next test.
7. Getting a low grade in the class would have hurted his grade point average.
8. He shaked off his sleepiness and stayed up into the morning hours to study.
9. He has wrote an outline for each chapter in the textbook.
10. The test had began when the bell rang.

Underline main verbs once and auxiliary verbs twice in the following sentences.

EXAMPLE:

Jane <u>might</u> <u>talk</u> to Mark.

a. Jimmy Carter was elected president in 1976..
b. He defeated President Gerald Ford in the 1976 presidential election.
c. President Ford would have been president again if President Carter had lost the election.
d. President Carter was known for his informality.
e. The Panama Canal Treaty was ratified by the senate during Carter's time in office.

1. In a democracy, power is vested in the people.
2. People in a democracy might rule directly.
3. More commonly, people in a democracy will elect representatives.
4. These representative can rule for the people.
5. Some countries, such as Britian and Sweden, have combined a democracy with a monarchy in their governments.
6. Last week, I found a great apartment in the city.
7. I was looking for what seemed like months.
8. The former tenant of the apartment got a job in another city and is moving out in two weeks.
9. I am asking several friends to help me with the move.
10. Soon I will become the interior designer of my very own home.

GRAMMAR BASICS: 40d—Irregular Verbs and Using *lie* and *lay*

Revise verbs in the following sentences if necessary.

EXAMPLE:
fell
I ~~fall~~ down the stairs yesterday.

   a. Adam teached Jill how to fly a kite.
   b. Harris has already looked at the newspaper.
   c. Please lie the books on your desk.
   d. Maria had became frustrated when the door wouldn't open.
   e. Erwin wear a blue shirt yesterday.

   1. I awoken feeling refreshed.
   2. Sarah brought her notebook to the chemistry professor.
   3. Had you began to do the experiment?
   4. Sarah had already took two years of chemistry in college before switching majors.
   5. Our little group has now growed to become a real organization.
   6. While all this was going on, Erin just standed there and watched.
   7. Have you dealed out the cards yet?
   8. Have you lay the books on your desk?
   9. After the long walk, both dogs drank a lot of water and then lay down.
  10. We should have wore our uniforms.

GRAMMAR BASICS: 40e—Verb tense

Use the tense indicated in parentheses when revising the verb(s) in the following sentences.

EXAMPLE:

I see the sign.   (past)   I saw the sign.

a. I walk.   (future perfect)
b. I walk.   (past)
c. I walk.   (past perfect progressive)
d. I walk.   (present progressive)
e. I walk.   (future progressive)

1. They sing.   (future perfect)
2. They sing.   (future progressive)
3. They sing.   (future perfect progressive)
4. They sing.   (future)
5. They sing.   (past)
6. You eat.   (past perfect progressive)
7. You eat.   (past)
8. You eat.   (present perfect)
9. You eat.   (present perfect progressive)
10. You eat.   (present progressive)

GRAMMAR BASICS: 40e-g—Verb Tense, Mood, and Voice

Revise the verbs in the following sentences if necessary.

EXAMPLES:

The temperature has dropped since the clouds ~~cover~~ the sun.
(covered)

~~The seeing was done by me~~ that the clouds covered the sun.
(I saw)

   a. Joan of Arc was a French military leader in the fifteenth century who says that God spoke to her in voices.

   b. Shortly after the army she led forced the English troops to end their siege of Orleans in 1429, she watched the coronation of Charles VII.

   c. If Joan of Arc would have lived in the twentieth century, she probably would have been a religious or military leader.

   d. I wish that time travel was possible, so I could meet her.

   e. The meeting of Joan of Arc by me I would find interesting.

  1. The planet Neptune was discover in 1846.

  2. Before Neptune's discovery, astronomers observe that the planet Uranus sometimes sped up and sometimes slowed down as it orbited the sun.

  3. The astronomers theorizes that the gravitational pull of another planet caused this uneven movement.

  4. This theory was confirmed by the sighting of Neptune by astronomers.

  5. The planet Neptune is named after the Roman god of the sea, Neptune; astronomers use his fishing spear, the trident, as the planet's symbol.

  6. If you was interested in coming with us, I'd have taken you in my car.

  7. Unless Troy were to stop complaining and start working harder, he'll have to find another committee to join.

  8. The lecture series was attended by me and several other people.

  9. Tina will have become an amateur astronomer by the time she completed her training.

10. That tree would have been a lot stronger now if you would have pruned it properly.

GRAMMAR BASICS: 41—Singular and Plural Subjects

Underline singular subjects once and plural subjects twice in the following sentences.

EXAMPLE:

<u>Geronimo</u> was an Apache.

a. Under cover of night, the nocturnal creatures come out to hunt.
b. The library is still our most useful resource for research.
c. Twenty thousand people participated in the poll.
d. The entire class followed Georgina around the building.
e. Miguel has cooked many elaborate meals without using any recipes.

1. Economics was dominated by the doctrine of mercantilism for several hundred years after the decline of feudalism.
2. A nation's wealth, in this doctrine, was based mainly on the amount of gold and silver in the nation's treasury.
3. Accumulating gold and silver bullion, establishing colonies, developing a strong merchant marine, and encouraging mining and industry were all approaches nations used to develop favorable balances of trade.
4. All mercantilist countries of the Western world shared a common goal: to achieve a surplus of exports over imports in order to build the national wealth.
5. This doctrine encouraged European countries to develop colonial holdings in Asia, Africa, North America, and South America.
6. Hydrogen, the lightest of all the chemical elements, normally has as its atom one electron in orbit around one proton.
7. A star, as well as a hydrogen bomb, produces a fusion reaction that transforms hydrogen atoms into helium atoms.
8. This fusion releases huge amounts of energy.
9. On earth, hydrogen is usually found as a gas.
10. No other element in the universe is as abundant as hydrogen.

Revise the following sentences, if necessary, to make subjects and verbs agree.

EXAMPLE:

      are
They ~~is~~ talking.

a. Professor Osborne's book about medieval French writers have inspired many of us to read their works.
b. Some of the buses is overheated.
c. Across the street is a bus stop.
d. The worst part of riding a bus are the waiting.
e. Seventy-five cents are the current bus fare.

1. One of the team's weaknesses are its tendency to skip practices.
2. Neither an orange nor grapes appeals to me today.
3. One of the problems at the university are inadequate parking.
4. Liver and onions are not one of my favorite foods.
5. Each class I wanted to take were closed.
6. Marissa's station wagon, as well as Jaime's minivan, are big enough for all of us.
7. Neither Mike nor his two roommates is very ambitious.
8. Each of the lawns need to be mowed.
9. Five cups of flour are called for by the recipe.
10. Everyone in town know the mayor takes a long walk each morning.

Underline all pronouns in the following sentences.

EXAMPLE:

<u>I</u> said <u>it</u> <u>myself</u>.

  a. Edward says he likes artichokes.
  b. Edward bought some fresh artichokes for us at the market yesterday.
  c. They are not going to the movie tonight.
  d. Alicia doesn't want anyone to help her.
  e. It has taken them eight years to achieve this.

  1. Mercury is a silvery-white metallic element; it is poisonous.
  2. Although it is a metal, mercury is liquid at room temperatures.
  3. Mercury's melting point is about $-39°$ C; it turns to liquid at that temperature.
  4. Mercury is also called quicksilver.
  5. While they were working with it in the laboratory, Heather and Samita handled the mercury very carefully.
  6. Because the planet Mercury is so close to the sun, it is very hot.
  7. It is named after Mercury, who was the fleet-footed messenger of the Roman gods.
  8. Mercury, which goes around the sun in eighty-eight days, has the shortest orbit of all the planets in the solar system.
  9. We can occasionally see Mercury as a morning or an evening star.
10. This is a planet photographed by Mariner 10 in 1975.

GRAMMAR BASICS: 41a-f—Pronoun-Antecedent Agreement and Pronoun Reference

Revise the following sentences, if necessary, so that each pronoun clearly refers to and agrees with the correct antecedent.

EXAMPLE:

The   books
~~Each of the~~ students opened their ~~book~~.

a. Gilbert and Sullivan collaborated on many operettas; Gilbert wrote the lyrics and dialogue, and he wrote the music.
b. I like to study biological trivia; that is my major.
c. In Montana, they say that the cold keeps the riffraff out.
d. Either the compact disc player or the loudspeaker needs its wiring repaired.
e. The tour group has the afternoon off to spend as it chooses.

1. I waited at the bus stop until it came.
2. To be accepted into this orchestra, you have to excel at an audition.
3. It was the sharpshooter Calamity Jane that boasted of her adventures as a Pony Express rider and scout.
4. The umbrella that I want to buy is on sale.
5. Each of his fingers and toes had their own stretching routine.
6. This pair of gloves fit perfectly.
7. Each of the students wrote their own paper.
8. Everyone had the chance to select which game they would attend.
9. The audience settled into its seats as the curtain rose.
10. Every member of the audience were happy.

GRAMMAR BASICS: 42k-t—Pronoun Case

Revise pronouns in the following sentences if necessary.

EXAMPLE:

He
~~Him~~ and I are on the football team.

a. John, Sarah, and me ate the pizza.
b. The manager gave the box to Maria and I.
c. Us orchestra members practice frequently.
d. Who attended the concert?
e. The coach praised my friend and myself for our hard work.

1. She and him went to the concert.
2. The concert bored her and I.
3. She and myself were bored by the concert.
4. If you're going to the show with her and I, you'd better be ready in one hour.
5. To be honest, it was me who changed the schedule.
6. The committee selected Brenda and myself as co-chairpersons.
7. Whomever told you that was wrong.
8. Us runners on the track team will compete in the marathon.
9. Whom has agreed to clean up after tonight's meeting?
10. He told his stupid jokes to my sister and myself.

Underline all adjectives in the following sentences.

EXAMPLE:

She felt <u>happy</u>.

  a. The old car is rusty.
  b. My grandfather is elderly but healthy.
  c. The car—old, rusty, and decrepit—belongs to my grandfather.
  d. It was a fast car when he first bought it.
  e. It holds many memories for him.

  1. We wrapped the package in pink paper but the post office said we should have used brown paper.
  2. Unblanched celery is greener than blanched celery.
  3. Rondell wrote the most poetic description that we received.
  4. Betty's horse is strong.
  5. Betty's horse is stronger than Mike's horse.
  6. Betty's horse is the strongest horse on the entire team.
  7. Betty's large horse runs rapidly.
  8. I walk fast.
  9. I am fast.
10. These confusing directions have gotten us lost.

GRAMMAR BASICS: 43—Adverbs

Underline all adverbs in the following sentences.

EXAMPLE:

The cook felt <u>unusually</u> creative <u>today</u>.

   a. The fireplace was very hot.
   b. The high temperature for that day was twenty below zero.
   c. We regularly pushed huge maple logs into the fireplace.
   d. The wind rattled the windowpanes, and the snow swirled fiercely outside the house.
   e. The bare trees swayed ominously in the twilight.

  1. Mary's performance in the basketball game was truly memorable.
  2. She ran more rapidly than the other center.
  3. She also jumped higher than the other center.
  4. Mary played memorably.
  5. Mary played well.
  6. Many people believe that music is the most commonly understood language.
  7. A musician doesn't even have to play his or her instrument expertly.
  8. An amateur player can select an easy piece carefully and practice it often.
  9. Fortunately, I've worked hard on the song I'm to play tomorrow.
 10. I've also invited my best friends to be in the audience.

GRAMMAR BASICS: 43c-d—Using Adjectives and Adverbs

Revise adjectives and adverbs in the following sentences if necessary.

EXAMPLE:

         fewer

This cheesecake contains ~~less~~ calories than regular cheesecake.

  a. You painted the room beautiful.

  b. The children don't have no patience for this long bus ride.

  c. The children especially enjoyed the more dramatic exhibits at the museum.

  d. I can't return your book yet because I read slow.

  e. That lighthouse is the most brightest along this part of the coast.

  1. Beth is the most happy runner on the team.

  2. Beth ran rapid.

  3. She ran good.

  4. Beth took less drinks of water during the race than the other athletes.

  5. She ran the best race she has ever run.

  6. She won the race because the other runners didn't have no finishing kick.

  7. The trophy she won looks well in her room.

  8. Even when she was in grade school, Beth was the most swift person in her class.

  9. She was more swifter than her brother.

10. She was the most swiftest runner in sixth grade.

Review exercises for G Grammar Basics appear at the end of C Correct Sentences.

Underline count nouns once and noncount nouns twice in the following sentences.

EXAMPLE:

<u>Oxygen</u> is <u>a</u> gas.

a. Hot air rises.
b. Hot air balloons rise.
c. I packed my clothing in the suitcase.
d. I packed my equipment in the bag.
e. I would like a cup of coffee, please.

1. We will ride our bicycles to the pool.
2. Did you listen to the radio?
3. Biology is my major.
4. My major is biology.
5. I enjoyed the play.
6. We are having pasta tonight.
7. I am boiling 4 quarts of water for making spaghetti.
8. Did you bring your luggage?
9. I am attending classes to gain knowledge.
10. Do you have an umbrella with you?

Change the verbs in the following sentences from singular to plural or from plural to singular if necessary.

EXAMPLE:

Chess ~~are~~ ^{is} a challenging game.

    a. If you want to see my drawings, they is in the next room.
    b. Ice are cold.
    c. The snows this winter have closed the schools for almost two weeks between December and March.
    d. My shoes is wet.
    e. The sunshine are too bright for me this morning.

  1. Rice are a staple of many people's diet.
  2. Chinese are a language spoken by two of my friends.
  3. Eggs is used in many baked goods.
  4. This house are large enough for my entire family.
  5. My clothing are in my suitcase.
  6. Computer science are my major.
  7. One of my most important possessions are my appointment book.
  8. Several books is necessary for this class.
  9. Aluminum are a metal.
10. The coffee is bitter.

Add or delete determiners in the following sentences if necessary.

EXAMPLE:

Are there ~~the~~ computer terminals in this room?

a. Did you plant flowers in garden?
b. I was first person to complete all requirements.
c. The tomatoes are tasty in salads.
d. This rice tastes good.
e. He has a few sheets of a paper.

1. The university has built new library.
2. One of books for this course was very expensive.
3. Are you wearing the different glasses today?
4. There are still many unknown plants in rainforest.
5. Our bicycles are parked on sidewalk.
6. Her car is so old that it is valuable.
7. She has the curly hair.
8. Did we get lot of rain?
9. We saw first movie.
10. Students who succeed take a pride in their schoolwork.

Add or delete articles in the following sentences if necessary.

EXAMPLE:

The teacher brought umbrella into classroom.
          ^an   ^the

a. It was a honor to receive an award.
b. It is not necessary to lick the postage stamps we use today.
c. My grandfather served on the battleship U.S.S. *Missouri*.
d. Answering machine took message for me while I was out.
e. We need to get larger pot for the meals we cook.

1. I sat on cold, metal chair.
2. We went to the store to buy an box of cereal.
3. Clouds are covering the sun.
4. The robins are migratory birds.
5. Desk in my office is made of oak.
6. I need new computer to run new program I just bought.
7. My father planted the onions in his garden last week. We will eat the onions in a couple of months.
8. Before the arrival of the European explorers, Incas created a great civilization in South America.
9. The serenity is a good state of mind to achieve.
10. The soccer is very popular sport in our area.

Cross out misplaced words in the following sentences. Then mark a caret (^) to show where each word belongs, and write the word in above the caret.

EXAMPLE:

wear
Should ~~wear~~ I my red big coat?
    ^

a. When should leave we?
b. Are my blue new slacks in the closet?
c. Yesterday, I bought the three last tickets for the concert.
d. Never we've heard this band before.
e. I'm very excited about attending the concert.

1. How did you the concert like?
2. Why did you walk out of the concert?
3. She asked me why did I walk out of that concert.
4. Did he drive his red big new car to the concert?
5. The first song that the band played was loud and happy very.
6. When the concert was over, we had a time hard deciding what to do next.
7. Finally, we agreed to go to a restaurant and get to eat something.
8. It took a time long to settle on a restaurant we would all like.
9. It was late at night, but anyway I wanted to have breakfast.
10. Nilda let me have a bite of her cheesecake, and delicious it was.

Underline adjectives once and adverbs twice in the following sentences.

EXAMPLE:

The <u>big</u> dog ran <u>rapidly</u>.

a. It was a windy day, so Nick ran carefully.
b. I drank orange juice first, and then I ate two eggs.
c. We wandered slowly down the rugged coastline.
d. I was nervous as he set up the computer network in our home.
e. Fortunately, we were able to reserve a big cabin on the lake.

1. They ran in a short race yesterday.
2. The yellow parrot squawked loudly.
3. He always wears white socks when playing basketball.
4. I never saw that popular movie.
5. I reluctantly sold my large house.
6. Sometimes I wonder if I need such an expensive car.
7. It was the last show of the night and Lydia was last in line.
8. I often think of my older sister.
9. I rarely go fishing in that small boat.
10. I don't have time to read this long book.

Substitute a correct preposition for any preposition used incorrectly in the following sentences. Then, delete any misplaced preposition, reinserting it in the correct position.

EXAMPLE:

When we meet <s>at</s> ^on^ Saturday, I will introduce you to my parents.

a. I'll know much more about this subject on a few weeks.
b. Will you be prepared bad weather for on your trip?
c. Make sure to go all the instructions over first.
d. We're going to meet the corner at Oak Street and of Main Road.
e. Please take one last look the room around before we leave.

1. I'll have a birthday on a couple of weeks.
2. I'll have a party at the evening in my birthday.
3. I'll have the party at my apartment.
4. My apartment is in the brick building in the corner of Oak Drive and Fifth Street.
5. I need to figure which games we'll play at the party out.
6. Will you help me call our friends on the West Coast up to find out if they will be able to attend?
7. I'll speak half of them with, and you can speak the other half of them with.
8. I've made a list so we won't leave out any of our friends.
9. We should go the list over one last time to make sure we didn't omit anybody.
10. Should we look renting a movie into for the party?

MULTILINGUAL WRITERS: 48—Gerunds and Infinitives

Underline gerunds once and infinitivess twice in the following sentences.

EXAMPLE:

Shall we go <u>to see</u> a movie?

a. We like to play cards after lunch.
b. We particularly enjoy playing bridge.
c. Do you promise to play bridge sometime?
d. We plan to play cards again on Friday.
e. We will try to play for an hour.

1. The goldfish seem to want more food.
2. I understand feeding them if they seem hungry.
3. Would you recommend feeding them more?
4. The pet store manager suggested feeding them this amount.
5. Maybe we can go to visit the manager and ask.
6. He liked eating at the elegant restaurant but does not want to go there again.
7. I want to give my old bicycle to Jeff.
8. She put off opening the curtains until he woke up.
9. The aquarium's sea lions are fascinating the children.
10. Please don't forget to bring my CD when you come today.

MULTILINGUAL WRITERS: 48—Gerunds and Infinitives

Change gerunds to infinitives or infinitives to gerunds in the following sentences if necessary.

EXAMPLE:

I enjoy ~~to play~~ basketball.
(playing)

a. I finished to write the paper this morning.
b. I enjoyed to write the paper.
c. A student asked handing in her paper tomorrow.
d. The teacher gave the student permission to hand in her paper tomorrow.
e. The student intends finishing her next paper on time.

1. I want going to the park today.
2. I remember seeing you in class last week.
3. Jeffrey is unable cooking dinner as he had promised.
4. I don't mind to wait another ten minutes.
5. My uncle needs to go to shop at the mall this afternoon.
6. Will you please help me figuring out the bus connections to the theater?
7. Do you recommend to take the 12-A bus to Third Avenue?
8. I recall to take this bus recently.
9. I promise buying the tickets early.
10. Should we plan leaving at 3:30?

Follow the directions in parentheses when revising the verb(s) in the following sentences.

EXAMPLE:

can
I shut the door. (present ability)
^

a. I leave to go home early today. (present preference)
b. I leave to go home early today. (future advisability)
c. I leave to go home early today. (present negative ability)
d. I leave to go home early today. (plan)
e. I leave to go home early today. (present ability)

1. I read the book. (future necessity)
2. I read the book. (past advisability)
3. I read the book. (present advisability)
4. I read the book. (good advice)
5. I read the book. (possibility)
6. I live in Nebraska. (past possibility)
7. I live in Nebraska. (present preference)
8. I live in Nebraska. (past preference)
9. I live in Nebraska. (past plan)
10. I live in Nebraska. (past habit)

Add or delete commas in the following sentences if necessary.

EXAMPLE:

The seven deadly sins are ~~anger~~ ^{anger,} covetousness (greed), envy, gluttony, lust, pride, and sloth.

a. Myopia or nearsightedness is a visual defect.
b. For myopic people distant objects appear blurred.
c. A myopic person's eyes focus light in front of the retina but a nonmyopic person's eyes focus light on the retina.
d. A person who wears glasses or contact lenses may be myopic.
e. For example I am severely myopic and I wear glasses.

1. The word, *deadline* was first used during the Civil War.
2. In Andersonville the Confederate guards could shoot prisoners who crossed a boundary line several feet inside the outer wall.
3. A deadline originally was a physical line not to be crossed but now, nearly 150 years later it is a line in time not to be crossed.
4. "For truth there is no deadline" wrote Heywood Broun.
5. *The Nation* published Broun's article on December 30 1939.
6. Writers who can meet deadlines.
7. Romy Arnold Ph.D. is writing a book on the uses of eclipses for astronomical purposes.
8. The bus took us northward through New York, and Connecticut then eastward toward Boston which we went around and then northward again, to Maine.
9. Even though it was raining heavily, there were more than 46000 people at the baseball stadium on opening day.
10. You received the e-mail I sent to you yesterday didn't you?

PUNCTUATION: 50—Commas

Add or delete commas in the following sentences if necessary.

EXAMPLE:

Light heavyweight boxers weigh between ~~160,~~ and 175 pounds.
  (160 written above 160,)

a. Although, Canada's area is 4,000,000 square miles, its population is under 30,000,000 people.
b. Canada produces large quantities of wheat, and beef.
c. Much of Canada lies in the harsh, northern latitudes.
d. Copper, gold, nickel, and zinc, are some of the abundant minerals in Canada's reserves.
e. Winnipeg, Manitoba, is home for one of the best ballet companies in North America.

1. Miss Muffet sat on a tuffet, and ate curds and whey.
2. Miss Muffet apparently wanted to sit on the tuffet, but, a spider frightened her away.
3. During her subsequent trial for assault, Miss Muffet testified that, she returned to the tuffet with a can of Raid to retaliate against the spider which had sat down beside her.
4. Miss Muffet, who was little, sat on a tuffet.
5. Little, Miss Muffet sat on a tuffet.
6. Out of all my friends Kevin, whom I consider my "computer geek" is special.
7. Once Kevin starts working on a problem with my computer he never stops until the problem is solved even if it takes all night.
8. Sometimes it takes all night and I regret having called Kevin, in the first place.
9. At first he usually says, that this fix will be easier, than he thought it would be.
10. In the end he usually ends up by calling the computer company's technical support which I could have done myself.

Delete commas in the following sentences if necessary.

EXAMPLE:

The oak tree that I planted two years ago, is growing.
The oak tree that I planted two years ago is growing.

a. After Evan listened to the tape of her lecture, three times, he said that, "it's impossible to understand."
b. However, he also said, "I'm going to go back, and read the chapter again until I understand it."
c. Doctors, who take the Hippocratic oath, pledge to do no harm.
d. On July 4, 1776, an upstart group of colonists, had the courage to declare their independence from the most powerful nation on the earth.
e. If you guessed, that there are 693, beans in this big glass jar, you're right.

1. The child held the spoon, intently.
2. The, small restless crowd waited for the fireworks display.
3. The display featured, many of the same fireworks used every year.
4. The pattern named, "Attitude,' has exactly the colors that we want.
5. Although, the professor talked about the next test, few students listened to him.
6. I laughed, and cried during the movie.
7. I laughed, cried, and then laughed again, during the movie.
8. I laughed, because the movie was funny.
9. Because the movie was sad, I cried.
10. He walked, against the traffic, rather than with it.

PUNCTUATION: 51—Semicolons

Revise the following sentences if necessary by adding or deleting semicolons, by substituting semicolons for other marks of punctuation, or by substituting other marks of punctuation for semicolons.

EXAMPLE:

We biked 80 miles ~~today,~~ the workout was superb.

(today;)

a. The committee included Jim Smith, the new accountant, Sarah Jones, the coordinator of the advertising division, and Tracy Youngblood, the director of public relations.

b. "For tomorrow," the professor in my Bible as Literature class said, "read Genesis 1:1–10; Psalm 23:1–6; and Job 1:1–10."

c. Stephen A. Douglas was a nineteenth-century political leader, however, he is best known today as the man who twice ran against Abraham Lincoln.

d. Douglas won the race against Lincoln to be senator from Illinois in 1858, he lost the race against Lincoln for the presidency in 1860.

e. The two men debated slavery in 1858; these debates are still remembered as the Lincoln-Douglas Debates.

1. Ben learned how to ride his bicycle fairly easily, he used training wheels.

2. At first, he was very shaky on the bike, he'd often scream, "I'm going to fall," a prophesy which usually came true immediately.

3. At these times; I would encourage him to get up and try again, I had seen what happened when training wheels were taken away from kids too soon.

4. The plumber said, "The leaky faucet is easy to fix, the corroded pipe is a bigger concern."

5. Then he added, "I can take care of all this now, but I recommend finding out what caused the corrosion."

6. Shakespeare wrote *Antony and Cleopatra; As You Like It; Hamlet; Julius Caesar, King Lear,* and *Macbeth.*

7. Shakespeare was born in Stratford-on-Avon, however, he spent most of his career in London.

8. He worked as an actor; playwright; and manager of the Globe Theater.

9. He spent his retirement back in Stratford; where he died in 1616.

10. The *First Folio;* the earliest collected edition of his plays; was published in 1623.

Revise the following sentences if necessary by adding or deleting colons, by substituting colons for other marks of punctuation, or by substituting other marks of punctuation for colons.

EXAMPLE:

sure: The
Of this I am ~~sure, the~~ car will give you trouble within three months.

a. Imitating the title of Stephen W. Hawking's book *A Brief History of Time: From the Big Bang to Black Holes,* my brother called his paper *A Brief History of My Time in the Chemistry Lab: From Unknown Chemicals to Unknown Chemicals.*
b. I woke up at 6,45 in the morning.
c. After my brother and his friends have been in the kitchen, I know what the refrigerator will look like, empty.
d. Our street has: many potholes, bumps, and big cracks in it.
e. Our country has the oldest national park in the world, Yellowstone National Park.

1. You will succeed at this job if you: get here on time, follow instructions, and check your work carefully.
2. I will never forget the first time I tried to ski: I fell in the middle of the slope, and I struggled for twenty minutes to get up.
3. The Queen of Hearts, in Lewis Carrolls' *Alice's Adventures in Wonderland,* has an easy but gruesome answer whenever anyone bothers her, "Off with her head! Off with his head!"
4. Janice's time for this race was 26,42,09.
5. We ran into a lot of problems getting here, including: too few toll booths at the bridge, road construction closing all but one lane, and just too much traffic.
6. In Richard Brinsley Sheridan's play *The Rivals*, Mrs. Malaprop says: "He is the very *pineapple* of politeness."
7. She means: *pinnacle.*
8. A malapropism today is: a word misused as Mrs. Malaprop might have used it.
9. When my roommate and I went to see *The Rivals*: we laughed louder than the other people in the audience.
10. People turned and looked: at us.

PUNCTUATION: 51-52—Semicolons and Colons

Revise the following sentences if necessary by adding or deleting semicolons or colons, by substituting semicolons or colons for other marks of punctuation, or by substituting other marks of punctuation for semicolons or colons.

EXAMPLE:

                                    including the
The Acropolis is the site of famous ruins, ~~including: The~~ Parthenon.

   a. Although Steven Spielberg established his reputation by making adventure films; he made *Schindler's List*, which was based on historic fact, in 1993.
   b. These adventure films include: *Raider's of the Lost Ark* (1981) and *E.T.* (1982).
   c. Spielberg was known for his adventure films, nevertheless, he earned critical acclaim and popular success with *Schindler's List*.
   d. Joe Swensen won the election for mayor by a margin of 3;1.
   e. This memo is addressed to: Ms. Reese and it is from: Mr. Brand.

   1. Body language includes: gestures and eye contact.
   2. The American gesture for "okay" involves forming a circle with the forefinger and thumb, this gesture means: "zero" in France.
   3. The American gesture for "okay" has various meanings in other cultures, such as: "zero" in France, "money" in Japan, and a vulgarity in Brazil.
   4. Business people in foreign countries need to understand that body language has various meanings depending on culture, otherwise, they may offend prospective customers.
   5. Although looking someone in the eye means honesty in the United States and Canada; in most Asian and Latin American countries, it might mean aggression or ill breeding.
   6. Asian business people tend to prefer: brief or no handshakes, sitting side by side during negotiations, and long negotiations.
   7. In contrast to business people in the Middle East, who usually stand about 2 feet apart when talking; business people in the United States and Canada usually stand about 5 feet apart.
   8. When I wash my car, I always follow the same steps, wet, gently rub, and dry the car's exterior, pick up the papers, food, and other trash from the floor, and clean the carpets, dashboard, and windows.
   9. Anthea is especially eager to go on this trip: It will be her first time in another country.
   10. The Amateur Astronomy course teaches several skills, such as: grinding a telescope's lens, selecting the right telescope, choosing where to go to look at the sky, and how to use a sky chart.

Add or delete apostrophes in the following sentences if necessary. Word changes may be necessary, as in the example.

EXAMPLE:

My roommate, ~~who's~~ whose talents do not include cooking, can barely boil water.

a. Mexicos area is 761,000 square miles.
b. Its population in 1993 was 84.4 million.
c. In 1992, the population of Mexico City, Mexico's capital, was nearly nine million, while New York Citys population in 1992 was about seven million.
d. Mexico Citys larger than New York City.
e. Mexico City's and New York City's traffic jams are legendary.

1. Texas' nickname is "The Lone Star State."
2. Every one of these computer's hard drives is full.
3. How many *is* appear in *Mississippi*?
4. Gilbert's and Sullivan's operettas include *H.M.S. Pinafore* and *The Mikado*.
5. Gilbert and Sullivan wrote their operetta's in the late 1800s.
6. The music is difficult, so only experienced singers' can sing the lead roles.
7. You just spilled coffee on my supervisors' desk.
8. I don't like your using all those &s; instead, please use the word and in each case.
9. I borrowed my father-in-laws' car.
10. Cat's were sitting in the house.

PUNCTUATION: 54—Quotation Marks

Add or delete quotation marks and revise other punctuation in the following sentences if necessary. Also revise any tired or inappropriate language enclosed in quotation marks in the following sentences.

EXAMPLE:

In a speech he gave in Detroit on June 23, 1963, Martin Luther King, Jr., said,

"If a man hasn't discovered something that he will die for, he isn't fit to live."
live".

a. Dr. Kramer presented the award to Nicholas and said, "You have earned this important award by distinguishing yourself in activities including academics, leadership, the arts, and social action".
b. Were we supposed to listen to Bach's Brandenburg Concerto Number 2?"
c. Many people confuse lie and lay.
d. The encyclopedia's entry titled "Very Large Array explains that the Array is located in New Mexico, and it is the largest radio telescope in the world.
e. Thomas Gray's poem "Elegy Written in a Country Churchyard" contains the line "The paths of glory lead but to the grave."

1. In his Inaugural Address, John F. Kennedy challenged all Americans by saying, "Ask not what your country can do for you; ask what you can do for your country."
2. In his famous pamphlet "Common Sense", Thomas Paine wrote, The cause of America is in a great measure the cause of all mankind."
3. In "Whom says so?" in *The Nation*, June 8, 1985, Calvin Trillin writes, 'As far as I'm concerned, "whom" is a word that was invented to make everyone sound like a butler'.
4. I asked Mary, Why did you name your pickup "Buck?"
5. "Because, Mary said, people pass it so often."
6. I like the Latin proverb *Ars longa, vita brevis* (life is short, art is long").
7. Chaucer translated the proverb as The life so short, the art so long to learn.
8. Please do not write "complements when you mean "compliments".
9. The scholarship I received from the service club was "only a drop in the bucket," but I thanked the club president "from the bottom of my heart."
10. "Defamation" is a false and malicious statement, one communicated to others, that injures a person's reputation; "defamation" in writing is "slander."

Correct end punctuation in the following sentences if necessary.

EXAMPLE:

We wondered if we would make it to the airport on time~~?~~ .

   a. Do you think I was wrong to order that CD over the Internet.
   b. The online order form I had to fill out was rather complicated! I obediently filled it the whole form! Then I submitted it!
   c. I gave my correct mailing and e-mail addresses, but I used a fake name: "John Jones."
   d. A confirmation e-mail message told me that I should receive the CD the next day, but I doubted that it was true?
   e. Now it's three days later and still no CD, so what should I do? Send the company an e-mail message? Call the company to complain? Wait a few more days?

   1. My friend is a quiet (?) person.
   2. "The mighty Oz has spoken."
   3. "I'm melting," wailed the Wicked Witch of the West. "I'm melting."
   4. The umpire barked, "Play ball."
   5. I wanted to know whether the umpire yelled "Play ball?"
   6. Did you hear the umpire yell "Play ball?"
   7. People of earth, lay down your weapons and prepare to be conquered.
   8. We asked the invaders if earth conquest meant the end of sports as we knew it?
   9. Of all the nations on earth, only tiny Monaco (!) resisted the extraterrestrial invaders.
  10. Give me liberty or give me death.

PUNCTUATION: 56—Other Punctuation Marks

Add or delete punctuation marks in the following sentences if necessary.

EXAMPLE:

Catcher in the Rye was published during the same general period in American literature as *Catch-22*, but the two ~~(2)~~ novels differ significantly in several ways.

a. Pandora opened the box that Zeus had given her—so the story goes—and let loose all the evils and miseries that now afflict humanity.

b. Some bacteria those that live in the digestive tract and aid digestion, for example are beneficial to humans.

c. Mark Twain's *The Adventures of Huckleberry Finn* contains lines I like, such as "There was (sic) things he stretched, but mainly he told the truth."

d. In her poem "Chahinkapa Zoo," Louise Erdrich writes about the frustration wild animals in zoos must feel (but can animals really feel frustration); the poem begins, "It is spring. Even here / The bears emerge from poured caverns. / Already their cubs have been devoured / by the feather-footed lynx caged next door."

e. Be sure to use only 1 / 3 of a cup of flour for that recipe.

1. They love Italian food, minestrone soup, pasta, and grated hard cheese.

2. The business manager ordered 30 (thirty) soccer balls for next season.

3. The agenda for the Midtown Car Club meeting includes 1 considering whether we should rent the garage, 2 recruiting new members, and 3 considering whether we should buy new tires at this time.

4. Although the ceremony was disappointing, (They could have at least mentioned your name) the dinner was delicious.

5. This circuit on the computer is hard-wired, built to do a specific job, so it needs no program to function properly.

6. Although some fears appear to be hard-wired into some animal brains, (falling, for example), we do not understand the brain well enough to say conclusively that it functions exactly like a computer.

7. To best approach a play by Shakespeare that is new to you, I suggest the following steps: 1 read the play for a general idea of what it's about, 2 listen to the play on tape or recording as you read it to understand the words, and 3 read it again in depth.

8. She opened her presentation by noting that she had some knowledge of gardening with native plants, she has written three books on the subject, and she explained in detail how advantageous it was in her own garden.

9. Because of General Grant's success on the battlefield in the closing days of the Civil War, President Lincoln was willing to overlook the Union

commander's fondness for whiskey. "Find out what brand he's drinking," Lincoln quipped when told of Grant's alcoholism, "and send a case to all our other generals."

10. To bring the Civil War to a quick conclusion, President Lincoln once proposed that "[We] find out what brand of whiskey Grant is drinking and send a case to all our other generals."

MECHANICS: 57—Hyphens

Revise the hyphens in the following sentences if necessary.

EXAMPLE:

The final test will be all inclusive.
The final test will be all-inclusive.

a. There were four to one odds against the home team.
b. The society was dominated by antiindustrialists.
c. Each of the graduated bowls that make a glass harmonica will produce a belllike tone of a particular pitch when you press your finger to its moistened rim.
d. The play director asked all cast members to redress for a group picture.
e. The more-expensive coat is the better-looking coat.

1. A short tempered umpire officiated at our baseball game.
2. A pint is one half of a quart.
3. The company's detailed training has created a well equipped sales force.
4. The car assigned to me has a barely-operating motor.
5. Lauren is now my ex-roommate.
6. The Milky Way is 100,000 light years in diameter.
7. President elect Jones spoke to us.
8. Anti-intellectual students will not enjoy Ms. Smith's class.
9. A toaster running for one hour will normally use one kilowatt hour of electricity.
10. The Smiths are a happily-married couple.

Add or delete capitals in the following sentences if necessary.

EXAMPLE:

In her book *The Warrior Woman*, Maxine Hong Kingston writes, "~~my~~ ^My^ aunt haunts me—her ghost drawn to me because now, after fifty years of neglect, I alone devote pages of paper to her, though not origamied into houses and clothes."

a. Michael's business was prospering, so he decided to run for Senator.
b. Many people in the state remember that he had won the Heisman trophy, an accomplishment his opponent, Senator Cummins, could not match.
c. He launched his campaign in Hickory County, where he grew up.
d. Eventually he visited every county in the state during his Senatorial Campaign.
e. In his victory speech as senator elect, he told his supporters that "You will always be proud of your vote for me, not because of what I say on your behalf, but because of what I do on your behalf."

1. If threatened, a horned toad has a unique defense: It squirts blood at its adversaries from a place near its eyes.
2. In addition to the spines on their bodies, horned toads have four forms of defense: (1) Blending into the environment, (2) Inflating to appear larger, (3) Running away, and (4) Squirting blood.
3. "Horned toads," the biology professor explained, "Are actually lizards, not toads."
4. Horned toads are native to the band of land extending from Southern British Columbia to Northern Guatemala.
5. Horned toads, like other reptiles, are Ectotherms—their body temperature rises and falls with the temperature of their environment.
6. George S. Patton, Jr., was an American General during World War II.
7. Patton led the third army's sweep across France and into Germany.
8. Patton, known for his forceful leadership, was nicknamed "old blood and guts."
9. "I have come to consider myself," Patton wrote in his diary, "as a sort of chip floating down a river of Destiny."
10. Patton is an important figure in recent History.

Either add or remove underlining (which signifies italic type) or quotation marks in the following sentences if necessary.

EXAMPLE:

I frequently eat bean <u>burritos</u> for lunch.
I frequently eat bean burritos for lunch.

a. In his book <u>Blue Highways</u>, William Least Heat Moon published an account of the trip he took around the United States in an old van he called "Ghost Dancer."
b. We traveled in a <u>Boeing 747</u>.
c. I told him to get here <u>pronto</u>.
d. She read about it in "Newsweek."
e. <u>In a Station in the Metro</u> is a famous two-line poem by Ezra Pound.

1. Zora Neale Hurston's "Their Eyes Were Watching God" is now generally considered to be one of the best American novels written in the twentieth century.
2. Georgia O'Keeffe's painting "The Winter Road, 1963" is reproduced in full color in the book "Georgia O'Keeffe."
3. Alice Walker published her novel "The Color Purple" in 1982.
4. You can find some college newspapers online, such as the Harvard Crimson.
5. The movie Catch Me If You Can is based on a true story of someone who successfully pretended to be an airline pilot, lawyer, and doctor when he was nineteen years old.
6. Irving Berlin dedicated all of the royalties for his song God Bless America to the Boy and Girl Scouts of America.
7. Do you like *sushi*?
8. I nearly wrote that the singer "brought the house down," but I didn't—I wanted to avoid using a <u>cliché</u>.
9. Don't say "goodbye"; this is just "au revoir."
10. Have you heard any of Verdi's <u>operas</u>?

MECHANICS: 60—Abbreviations

Revise the abbreviations and punctuation marks in the following
sentences if necessary.

EXAMPLE:

The concert will begin at 7:30 p.m..
The concert will begin at 7:30 p.m.

a. While discussing the pessimism so pervasive in the fourteenth century
    (1300–1399 A.D.), Barbara Tuchman writes in her book *A Distant Mirror*,
    "Death is not treated poetically as the soul's flight to reunion with God; it is a
    skeleton grinning at the vanity of life."
b. Dr. Alan Tolson, Ph.D., first proposed the theory of transferability.
c. I asked my sister, who lives in Tucson, Arizona to mail the brochure to me.
d. Desiderius Erasmus was the leader during the Reformation who advocated
    studying the literature of ancient Greece and Rome, increasing personal piety,
    changing the Catholic Church, etc.
e. The Metropolitan Transportation Authority (MTA) operates most of the
    transit systems in the New York area, and many people believe the M.T.A.
    does a pretty good job.

1. My job starts at 8:30 A.M.
2. Julius Caesar introduced the Julian calendar in Rome in B.C. 46.
3. A yard equals 36 in.
4. Water freezes at 32° F.
5. Maj. Funding will never be promoted.
6. It seems that nearly everyone is recommending that I see Roald R. Sesila Jr.,
    M.D.
7. Here is the $48.33 I owe you for the theater tickets.
8. The Transco Tower, in Houston, TX, was designed by the famous American
    architect Philip Johnson.
9. J. Edgar Hoover served as director of the Federal Bureau of Investigation
    from 1924 until 1972.
10. Please send the bill to Oak St. NW, Somewhere, NJ.

MECHANICS: 61—Numbers

Revise numbers in the following sentences if necessary.

EXAMPLE:

1998 was a good year.
~~Nineteen-ninety-eight~~ was a good year.

a. Alfred E. Newman was born on April first, 1954.
b. World War II ended in Europe on May 8, 1945.
c. Uranium's melting point is 1,132 degrees C, and its boiling point is three thousand eight hundred and eighteen degrees C.
d. 143 people came to work on our arboretum cleaning day.
e. You'll find him at Eighteen Orchard Road, which is at the corner of Main Street.

1. You'll find Table C on page thirty-six.
2. When the package arrives, please make sure that we receive all sixty seven shirts.
3. Less than 40% of our members voted in the annual election of officers.
4. We'll meet at 3 o'clock.
5. We'll meet at 3 in the afternoon.
6. I've written 3-quarters of my paper.
7. Although we had 27 people working on our fund raising campaign, they only sold 39 magazine subscriptions and 19 plants.
8. A straight flush is ranked above four of a kind in poker.
9. An ounce is 1/sixteenth of a pound.
10. I listen to the radio station located at ninety-three point three on the FM dial.

REVIEW 1

Revise the following sentences for sentences and word options if necessary.

EXAMPLE:

     The   pitched

~~In fact, the~~ catcher ~~performed the action of pitching~~ batting practice.

a. Mr. Richardson and his wife, Jeanette Richardson, have agreed to host our holiday dinner.
b. After the track meet, the winners received their medals.
c. Even though Ted touched the poison ivy, he got a rash anyway.
d. The lion is an animal well designed for stalking, for chasing, and to overpower its prey.
e. The elephant fluted in triumph when it defeated its opponent.

1. Our representatives are debating the bill at the present time.
2. The bill expresses its author's wish to increase the speed limit.
3. Florida's capital is Tallahassee, and the capital of New Mexico is Santa Fe.
4. We left at the crack of dawn, so we could make the trip in one day.
5. Johann Pachelbel was a composer and organist in the 17th century. Johann Pachelbel wrote the famous <u>Canon in D Major</u>.
6. The average voter thinks his senator should reduce government waste.
7. A visit to the spectacular Maine woods is always an excruciating experience for us.
8. The sky grew not only light, but also the clouds in the east glowed many colors.
9. Finding a motel that will let you have your dog in the room with you is a major challenge. However, finding a hotel that will accept dogs is not an impossible challenge.
10. Leticia is having a difficult time learning how to swim and finds it hard to do.

REVIEW 2

Revise the following sentences if necessary.

EXAMPLE:

       wears

Batman ~~wear~~ a costume that hides his identity.

a. After the mixture boil for five minutes, it cool in the test tube.
b. If everyone in the country went shopping for a new car tomorrow, would they generally buy or lease?
c. There's no joy in Mudville: Mighty Casey has striked out.
d. The reason I got lost is because I was unfamiliar with the neighborhood.
e. Since he likes to ring doorbells, he started selling door-to-door.

1. When planning a vacation trip too much can take the fun and surprises out of it.
2. Have you chose the book you want to read?
3. Each picture I take and friendship I make has a touch of sorrow in it because they bring me a little closer to leaving.
4. *Honey, I Shrunk the Kids.*
5. To better understand the titles in computer games, Peter studying Japanese.
6. I won the competition, even though I skated bad.
7. My trumpet teacher told me that I only will get to the next level if I practice more.
8. The reason this sandwich is less tasty is because it was made without butter.
9. I like this sandwich better than the other sandwiches on the tray it was made with butter and mayonnaise.
10. The sandwich with butter and mayonnaise is the most fattening sandwich on the tray.

REVIEW 3

Revise the following sentences if necessary.

EXAMPLE:

tomorrow.
I should go to class ~~yesterday.~~

a. Everyone who came to the restaurant loved the orange fat cat that lived there.
b. "Queenie" her name was.
c. She pranced around the place as though she owned it.
d. Few people knew the real reason she were there.
e. It was keep the mice away.

1. One of the most important inventions of the twentieth century are television.
2. It brings the current events, the cultural events, and the entertainment into our homes.
3. The television set in my room are old.
4. I carefully moved it from the living room in my parents' house to my room.
5. I watch this television to keep up the news with.
6. I also enjoy to watch sports.
7. You should visit me on Sunday, so we can together watch the football game.
8. I was rather watch football than baseball.
9. Rice sounds like a good idea for dinner.
10. Should we flavor the rice with the curry?

REVIEW 4

Revise punctuation in the following sentences if necessary.

EXAMPLE:

The one cannibal said $\overset{\text{said,}}{\text{"I}}$ don't like your friend," and the second cannibal
$\overset{\text{said,}}{\text{said}}$ "That's okay, just eat the vegetables."

a. On July 20, 1969 Neil Armstrong became the first person to walk on the moon.
b. *Brillig* is a nonsense word which was coined by Lewis Carroll.
c. Chlorophyll makes plants green.
d. I followed the street as we were told to do: Jenny took a short cut through the park.
e. The Library of Congress, which was built in 1897, contains: 327 miles of bookshelves.

1. According to a study published in 1980 in *Public Health Reports*: The survival rate for people who were recovering from heart attacks and who owned pets was higher than the survival rate for people without pets.
2. The study, limited though it was, seems to show that having a pet helps a person recover from a heart attack.
3. The mortality rate for people owning pets' was about 1/3 that of the people who did not own pets.
4. One possible explanation is that: the pets helped their owners relax.
5. Many nursing homes, prisons, and mental institutions, now allow pets to interact with those individuals who are depressed, lonely, and unhappy.
6. When I first became the supervisor, I was so nervous that everyone had a secret name for me: Rattled.
7. When drawing a bow a person uses three fingers.
8. I work at the library, on Monday nights and Saturdays.
9. I always have the same answer to a rainy day. My umbrella.
10. The month of March is named after the planet "Mars."

REVIEW 5

Revise the following sentences if necessary.

EXAMPLE:
Five-hundred
500-pound canaries say, "Here kitty, here kitty."

a. The motion won by eighty six votes.
b. The bare walked back and forth all day long in its cage.
c. The nutritionist at our cafeteria is antivegetarian.
d. When Little Red Riding Hood comments on her grandmother's big tooths, the wolf (who is disguised as the grandmother) replies, "The better to eat you with!"
e. I read Shakespeare's "Hamlet" six times before I saw the play performed.

1. The *Monitor* and the *Merrimac* were the first two iron covered ships to fight a sea battle.
2. Ground-Hog Day is on Feb. 2 each year.
3. Ralph Waldo Emerson encouraged self reliance.
4. This is the best-fitting pair of shoes I have ever worn.
5. This pair costs only one half of what my other pair cost.
6. I road down the highway in your car.
7. He drove South on Elm Avenue.
8. Abraham Lincoln was President during the Civil War.
9. President Abraham Lincoln's Gettysburg Address is a masterpiece of prose poetry.
10. We read "Death of a Salesman."

Answers to Lettered Exercises

10f—Avoiding Logical Fallacies
a. Slippery slope.
b. Irrelevant argument.
c. False authority.
d. Slanted language.
e. Begging the question.

15—Conciseness (Possible answers)
a. I liked the movie.
b. The ambulance driver decided to ignore the red light.
c. The menu lists fifteen different sandwiches.
d. John, a good athlete, wants to play professional football.
e. The Speaker introduced the bill into the House.

15—Conciseness (Possible answers)
a. The house was large, old, and drafty.
b. With the endlessly conflicting reports of research studies on healthy dietary habits, it's difficult to know what we should be eating.
c. The bottom line shows profit or loss.
d. People often use the phrase "bottom line" to mean the determining consideration in a decision.
e. Correct.

16a–b—Coordination (Possible answers)
a. The French Revolution began in 1789; it ended France's thousand-year monarchy.
b. King Louis XVI assembled the French Parliament to deal with France's huge debt, and then the common people's part of Parliament proclaimed itself France's true legislature.
c. King Louis protested, so a crowd destroyed the royal prison.
d. A constitutional monarchy was established; some people thought the king would be content.
e. King Louis and the queen, Marie Antoinette, tried to leave the country, but they were caught, convicted of treason, and executed.

16c–d—Subordination (Possible answers)
a. The French Revolution, which began in 1789, ended France's thousand-year monarchy.
b. After King Louis XVI assembled the French Parliament to deal with France's huge debt, the common people's part of Parliament proclaimed itself France's true legislature.

c. When King Louis protested, a crowd destroyed the royal prison.
d. Because a constitutional monarchy was established, some people thought the king would be content.
e. When King Louis and the queen, Marie Antoinette, tried to leave the country, they were caught, convicted of treason, and executed.

17a—Parallelism (Possible answers)
a. Archimedes was an ancient Greek scientist, mathematician, and inventor.
b. According to legend, Archimedes is supposed to have said "Give me the place to stand and a lever long enough, and I will move the earth" and to have shouted "Eureka!" when he stepped into his bath and realized that he could measure the volume of an object by determining the volume of the water it displaces when submerged.
c. Archimedes discovered the principle of buoyancy, he discovered formulas for calculating the areas of various geometric figures, and he invented the Archimidean screw.
d. According to the principle of buoyancy, boats float and balloons rise because they weigh less than the water or air they displace.
e. Correct.

17e–h—Sentence Length and Sentence Variety (Possible answers)
a. My friend Barbara has a "hybrid" car that runs on both gasoline and electricity. It charges its battery whenever she uses the brakes.
b. The young man walked.
c. The man walked slowly.
d. The man walked with a spring in his step.
e. The man who wanted exercise walked.

11—Sentence Fragments (Possible answers)
a. Correct.
b. Today, *girl* denotes a female child. In Middle English, *girl* denoted a child of either sex. [verb *denotes* is also correct]
c. The word *balkanization* derives from the name of the Balkan Peninsula, which was divided into several small nations in the early twentieth century.
d. Bacteria, at times present in incorrectly canned or preserved foods, causes botulism, a type of food poisoning which is often fatal if not treated properly.
e. During the winter, many people use hand cream because their skin gets too dry.

12—Comma Splices and Run-on Sentences (Possible answers)
a. These days, a significant proportion of camera-buyers are opting for digital rather than conventional cameras. The cost of digital cameras has come down and the quality of their photos is steadily increasing.

b. Part of the purchase decision depends on determining whether the quality of digital photos is high enough. Photo quality depends on the photographer's taste and on the purpose of the photo.

c. For example, many people just want snapshots of their friends and family. This type of photography does not require an expensive, highly sophisticated digital camera.

d. Correct.

e. As in most things, the greater the capability of the digital camera, the more expensive it is. Fortunately, there is a wide range of capabilities from which to choose.

13—Shifting and Disjointed Sentences

a. I enjoy reading my horoscope, but I really wonder if it's ever true.

b. Keeping fit may not help you live longer, but it will make your later years more comfortable. Exercising regularly is good for you.

c. Standing inside the penalty area allows a soccer goalie to handle the ball.

d. My cousin Shawn, who is 35 years old, never learned to ride a bicycle.

e. I am emphasizing that you be more punctual because you have missed your train four days in a row.

14—Misplaced and Dangling Modifiers

a. Gradually, the members of the hiking group made their way to the trailhead.

b. Eager to get started, the hike leader quickly explained where they would be going.

c. Three hikers, expressing their concern, said that this was their first hike ever.

d. Correct.

e. Seven hours later, the tired but exhilarated group completed the challenging hike and celebrated at a local restaurant.

19b—Choosing Exact Words (Possible answers)

a. The gardener's skin was sunburned.

b. The basketball player is tall.

c. Her perfume has a wonderful scent.

d. I bought Carl's car.

e. Janet's house is 40 miles from here.

19d—Using Appropriate Language (Possible answers)

a. If you agree with Mr. Anderson's argument, then you're not thinking clearly.

b. I think I'll fail accounting.

c. Contemporaries often described the artist Vincent van Gogh as a good listener.

d. The door wouldn't close because the carpenters had hung it incorrectly.

e. Correct.

20—Gender-Neutral Language (Possible answers)
a. Jane is the new chairperson of our committee.
b. The Constitution gives every American freedom of speech.
c. Correct.
d. All police officers should be honest.
e. Mike cleaned, took care of the children, and cooked.

21—Spelling
a. Just remember that you're now among friends.
b. Can your restaurant accommodate a dinner party of 26 people?
c. It is relatively easy to learn to drive, but driving well requires experience.
d. Alyssa has had her driver's license for two years now.
e. I'd like to order some stationery for my new business.

21a—Spelling Plurals
a. Carl prefers his french fries without ketchup.
b. He was at two beaches yesterday.
c. Correct.
d. He wore shoes, so his feet are fine.
e. Carl is one of my brothers-in-law.

21b–c—Adding Suffixes and Spelling *ie, ei* words
a. The results of your survey are not statistically correct.
b. I believe I will have my hair cut.
c. Did you paint the ceiling?
d. Correct.
e. The company exceeded its sales goal for the year by the end of the first quarter.

21d—Spelling Homonyms
a. This is a tough decision to make, so we're asking for your counsel.
b. I accept the invitation.
c. We went to the state fair.
d. This schedule is altogether confusing.
e. It is better to recycle paper than to waste it.

21d—Spelling Commonly Confused Words
a. You can always spot me from afar by the clothes I'm wearing.
b. Cheese and milk are dairy products.
c. This is the quiet before the storm.
d. I can't discuss what Yusef told me because it's personal.
e. If you're ready to begin, you may proceed.

26g—Avoiding Plagiarism
a. Bill Gates was only 13 years old when he wrote his first software program.
b. Already an entrepreneur while in high school, he founded a company called Traf-O-Data, which marketed traffic-counting systems to local governments. He also helped form a group of programmers who put their school's payroll system on computer.
c. While a sophomore at Harvard University in 1975, Gates and Paul G. Allen, a friend from his hometown, developed software for early microcomputers.
d. At that time BASIC was the preferred programming language for large computers; they adapted BASIC for microcomputers.
e. Their success spurred Gates to leave Harvard while in his junior year, and he teamed with Allen to establish Microsoft.

29b—Using MLA Guidelines
a. Cayton, Andrew, et al. America: Pathways to the Present. Upper Saddle River, NJ: Prentice Hall, 2003.
b. Goldman, Edwin Franko, and Walter M. Smith, eds. Arban's Complete Conservatory Method for Trumpet. New York: Carl Fischer, 1982.
c. Olver, Lynne, and Christopher J. Chipello. "British Columbia Acts to Inject Market Forces Into Lumber Prices." Wall Street Journal. 27 March 2003: A2.
d. "Inline Efficiency." Popular Science March 2003: 22.
e. King, Nelson. "Add Organization to Outlook." PC Magazine 24 December 2002:48.

32b—Using APA Guidelines
a. Swartz. S. (1989, March 31). Why Michael Milken stands to qualify for Guinness Book. Wall Street Journal, 1.
b. Steele, R. (June 2000). Awful but lawful. Boating, 36.
c. Pinker, S. (2002). The blank slate. New York: Penguin Putnam.
d. Goldstein, E. B. (1999). Sensation and perception (5th ed.). Pacific Grove, CA: Brooks-Cole.
e. Greenfield, P.M. (1998). The cultural evolution of IQ. In U. Neisser (Ed.), The Rising Curve: Long-Term Gains in I@ and Related Measures (pp. 81-123). Washington, DC: American Psychological Association.

39j—Subjects and Verbs
Subject   Verb

a. The weather was delightfully mild yesterday.
b. Everyone went to the park to enjoy the day.
c. In fact, the park was too crowded.
d. We decided to make the best of it.
e. A quiet walk in the woods gave us some relief.

74

40a—Transitive and Intransitive Verbs
Transitive   Intransitive

a. I <u>saw</u> Helena at the gym this morning.
b. Her workout <u>was</u> long and strenuous.
c. Afterward, she <u>limped</u> back to the dressing room.
d. Maybe I <u>was</u> wrong, but I <u>offered</u> her some advice.
e. I <u>told</u> her to build up her strength before she <u>tries</u> another difficult workout.

40b—Regular and Irregular Verbs
a. Correct.
b. Have you ever dived off the high board?
c. The water in the pool was cold today.
d. Until recently, I would have sunk in water over my head.
e. I have grown stronger as a swimmer in recent weeks.

40c—Main and Auxiliary Verbs
Main   Auxiliary

a. Jimmy Carter <u>was</u> <u>elected</u> president in 1976.
b. He <u>defeated</u> President Gerald Ford in the 1976 presidential election.
c. President Ford <u>would have</u> <u>been</u> president again if President Carter <u>had</u> <u>lost</u> the election.
d. President Carter <u>was</u> <u>known</u> for his informality.
e. The Panama Canal Treaty <u>was</u> <u>ratified</u> by the Senate during Carter's time in office.

40b, 40d—Irregular Verbs and Using *lie* and *lay*
a. Adam taught Jill how to fly a kite.
b. Correct.
c. Please lay the books on your desk.
d. Maria had become frustrated when the door wouldn't open.
e. Erwin wore a blue shirt yesterday.

40c—Verb Tense
a. I will have walked.
b. I walked.
c. I had been walking.
d. I am walking.
e. I will be walking.

40e–g—Verb Tense, Mood, and Voice
a. Joan of Arc was a French military leader in the fifteenth century who said that God spoke to her in voices.
b. Correct.
c. If Joan of Arc had lived in the twentieth century, she probably would have been a religious or military leader.
d. I wish that time travel were possible, so I could meet her.
e. It would be interesting to meet Joan of Arc.

41—Singular and Plural Subjects
Singular   Plural

a. Under cover of night, the nocturnal <u>creatures</u> come out to hunt.
b. The <u>library</u> is still our most useful resource for research.
c. Twenty thousand <u>people</u> participated in the poll.
d. The entire <u>class</u> followed Georgina around the building.
e. <u>Miguel</u> has cooked many elaborate meals without using any recipes.

41—Subject–Verb Agreement
a. Professor Osborne's book about medieval French writers has inspired many of us to read their works.
b. Some of the buses are overheated.
c. Correct.
d. The worst part of riding a bus is the waiting.
e. Seventy-five cents is the current bus fare.

42—Identifying Pronouns
a. Edward says <u>he</u> likes artichokes.
b. Edward bought some fresh artichokes for <u>us</u> at the market yesterday.
c. <u>They</u> are not going to the movie tonight.
d. Alicia doesn't want <u>anyone</u> to help <u>her</u>.
e. It has taken <u>them</u> eight years to achieve <u>this</u>.

42a–f—Pronoun-Antecedent Agreement and Pronoun Reference
a. Gilbert and Sullivan collaborated on many operettas; Gilbert wrote the lyrics and dialogue, and Sullivan wrote the music.
b. I like to study biological trivia; biology is my major.
c. In Montana, people say that the cold keeps the riffraff out.
d. Correct.
e. The tour group has the afternoon off to spend as they choose.

42k–t—Pronoun Case
a. John, Sarah, and I ate the pizza.
b. The manager gave the box to Maria and me.
c. We orchestra members practice frequently.

76

d. Correct.

e. The coach praised my friend and me for our hard work.

43—Adjectives

a. The <u>old</u> car is <u>rusty</u>.

b. My grandfather is <u>elderly</u> but <u>healthy</u>.

c. The car—<u>old</u>, <u>rusty</u>, and <u>decrepit</u>—belongs to <u>my</u> grandfather.

d. It was a <u>fast</u> car when he first bought it.

e. It holds <u>many</u> memories for him.

43—Adverbs

a. The fireplace was <u>very</u> hot.

b. The high temperature for that day was twenty below zero.

c. We <u>regularly</u> pushed huge maple logs into the fireplace.

d. The wind rattled the windowpanes, and the snow swirled <u>fiercely</u> outside the house.

e. The bare trees swayed <u>ominously</u> in the twilight.

43c–d—Using Adjectives and Adverbs

a. You painted the room beautifully.

b. The children don't have any patience for this long bus ride.

c. Correct.

d. I can't return your book yet because I read slowly.

e. That lighthouse is the brightest along this part of the coast.

44a—Count and Noncount Nouns

Count   <u>Noncount</u>

a. Hot <u>air</u> rises.

b. Hot air <u>balloons</u> rise.

c. I packed my <u>clothing</u> in the <u>suitcase</u>.

d. I packed my <u>equipment</u> in the <u>bag</u>.

e. I would like a <u>cup</u> of <u>coffee</u>, please.

44b—Singulars and Plurals

a. If you want to see my drawings, they are in the next room.

b. Ice is cold.

c. Correct.

d. My shoes are wet.

e. The sunshine is too bright for me this morning.

44b—Singulars and Plurals

a. Did you the plant flowers in the garden?

b. I was the first person to complete all the requirements.

c. Tomatoes are tasty in salads.

d. Correct.

e. He has a few sheets of paper.

45—Articles

a. It was an honor to receive an award.

b. Correct.

c. My grandfather served on the battleship the U.S.S. *Missouri*.

d. The answering machine took the message for me while I was out.

e. We need to get a larger pot for the meals we cook.

46—Word Order

a. When should we leave?

b. Are my new blue slacks in the closet?

c. Yesterday, I bought the last three tickets for the concert.

d. We've never heard this band before.

e. Correct.

46b–c—Adjectives and Adverbs

Adjective   Adverb

a. It was a <u>windy</u> day, so Nick ran <u>carefully</u>.

b. I drank orange juice <u>first</u>, and <u>then</u> I ate <u>two</u> eggs.

c. We wandered <u>slowly</u> down the <u>rugged</u> coastline.

d. I was <u>nervous</u> as he set up the <u>computer</u> network in our home.

e. <u>Fortunately</u>, we were able to reserve a <u>big</u> cabin on the lake.

47—Prepositions

a. I'll know much more about this subject in a few weeks.

b. Will you be prepared for bad weather on your trip?

c. Make sure to go over all the instructions first.

d. We're going to meet at the corner of Oak Street and Main Road.

e. Please take one last look around the room before we leave.

47—Gerunds and Infinitives

Gerund   Infinitive

a. We like <u>to play</u> cards after lunch.

b. We particularly enjoy <u>playing</u> bridge.

c. Do you promise <u>to play</u> bridge sometime?

d. We plan <u>to play</u> cards again on Friday.

e. We will try <u>to play</u> for an hour.

47—Gerunds and Infinitives

a. I finished writing the paper this morning.

b. I enjoyed writing the paper.

c. A student asked to hand in her paper tomorrow.
d. Correct.
e. The student intends to finish her next paper on time.

49—Modal Auxiliary Verbs
a. I would like to leave to go home early today.
b. I (should, ought to) leave to go home early today.
c. I cannot leave to go home early today.
d. I plan to leave to go home early today.
e. I can leave to go home early today.

50—Commas
a. Myopia, or nearsightedness, is a visual defect.
b. For myopic people, distant objects appear blurred.
c. A myopic person's eyes focus light in front of the retina, but a nonmyopic person's eyes focus light on the retina.
d. Correct.
e. For example, I am severely myopic and I wear glasses.

50—Commas
a. Although Canada's area is 4,000,000 square miles, its population is under 30,000,000 people.
b. Canada produces large quantities of wheat and beef.
c. Much of Canada lies in the harsh northern latitudes.
d. Copper, gold, nickel, and zinc are some of the abundant minerals in Canada's reserves.
e. Correct.

50—Commas
a. After Evan listened to the tape of her lecture three times, he said that "it's impossible to understand."
b. However, he also said, "I'm going to go back and read the chapter again until I understand it."
c. Doctors who take the Hippocratic oath pledge to do no harm.
d. On July 4, 1776, an upstart group of colonists had the courage to declare their independence from the most powerful nation on the earth.
e. If you guessed that there are 693 beans in this big glass jar, you're right.

51—Semicolons
a. The committee included Jim Smith, the new accountant; Sarah Jones, the coordinator of the advertising division; and Tracy Youngblood, the director of public relations.
b. "For tomorrow," the professor in my Bible as Literature class said, "read Genesis 1:1–10, Psalm 23:1–6, and Job 1:1–10."
c. Stephen A. Douglas was a nineteenth-century political leader; however, he is

best known today as the man who twice ran against Abraham Lincoln.

   d. Douglas won the race against Lincoln to be senator from Illinois in 1858; he lost the race against Lincoln for the presidency in 1860.

   e. Correct.

52—Colons

   a. Correct.

   b. I woke up at 6:45 in the morning.

   c. After my brother and his friends have been in the kitchen, I know what the refrigerator will look like: empty.

   d. Our street has many potholes, bumps, and big cracks in it.

   e. Our country has the oldest national park in the world: Yellowstone National Park.

51–52—Semicolons and Colons

   a. Although Stephen Spielberg established his reputation by making adventure films, he made *Schindler's List*, which was based on historic fact, in 1993.

   b. These adventure films include *Raider's of the Lost Ark* (1981) and *E.T.* (1982).

   c. Spielberg was known for his adventure films; nevertheless, he earned critical acclaim and popular success with *Schindler's List*.

   d. Joe Swensen won the election for mayor by a margin of 3:1.

   e. This memo is addressed to Ms. Reese and it is from Mr. Brand.

53—Apostrophes

   a. Mexico's area is 761,000 square miles.

   b. Correct.

   c. In 1992, the population of Mexico City, Mexico's capital, was nearly nine million, while New York City's population in 1992 was about seven million.

   d. Mexico City's larger than New York City.

   e. Mexico City and New York City's traffic jams are legendary.

54—Quotation Marks

   a. Dr. Kramer presented the award to Nicholas and said, "You have earned this important award by distinguishing yourself in activities including academics, leadership, the arts, and social action."

   b. Were we supposed to listen to Bach's "Brandenburg Concerto Number 2"?

   c. Many people confuse "lie" and "lay."

   d. The encyclopedia's entry titled "Very Large Array" explains that the Array is located in New Mexico, and it is the largest radio telescope in the world.

   e. Correct.

55—End Punctuation

   a. Do you think I was wrong to order that CD over the Internet?

   b. The online order form I had to fill out was rather complicated. I obediently filled it the whole form. Then I submitted it.`

c. Correct.

d. A confirmation e-mail message told me that I should receive the CD the next day, but I doubted that it was true.

e. Now three days have gone by and what should I do? send the company an e-mail message? call the company to complain? wait a few more days?

56—Other Punctuation Marks

a. Correct.

b. Some bacteria—those that live in the digestive tract and aid digestion, for example— are beneficial to humans.

c. Mark Twain's *The Adventure of Huckleberry Finn* contains lines I like, such as "There was [sic] things he stretched, but mainly he told the truth."

d. In her poem "Chahinkapa Zoo," Louise Erdrich writes about the frustration wild animals in zoos must feel (but can animals really feel frustration?); the poem begins, "It is spring. Even here/The bears emerge from poured caverns./Already their cubs have been devoured/by the feather-footed lynx caged next door."

e. Be sure to use only 1/3 of a cup of flour for that recipe.

57—Hyphens

a. There were four-to-one odds against the home team.

b. The society was dominated by anti-industrialists.

c. Each of the graduated bowls that make a glass harmonica will produce a bell-like tone of a particular pitch when you press your finger to its moistened rim.

d. The play director asked all cast members to re-dress for a group picture.

e. The more expensive coat is the better looking coat.

58—Capitals

a. Michael's business was prospering, so he decided to run for senator.

b. Many people in the state remember that he had won the Heisman Trophy, an accomplishment his opponent, Senator Cummins, could not match.

c. Correct.

d. Eventually he visited every county in the state during his senatorial campaign.

e. In his victory speech as senator-elect, he told his supporters that "you will always be proud of your vote for me, not because of what I say on your behalf, but because of what I do on your behalf."

59—Italics

a. Correct.

b. We traveled in a Boeing 747.

c. I told him to get here pronto.

d. She read about it in *Newsweek*.

e. "In a Station of the Metro" is a famous two-line poem by Ezra Pound.

60—Abbreviations

a. While discussing the pessimism so pervasive in the fourteenth century (A.D. 1300–1399), Barbara Tuchman writes in her book *A Distant Mirror*, "Death is not treated poetically as the soul's flight to reunion with God; it is a skeleton grinning at the vanity of life."

b. Dr. Alan Tolson first proposed the theory of transferability.

c. I asked my sister, who lives in Tucson, Arizona, to mail the brochure to me.

d. Desiderius Erasmus was the leader during the Reformation who advocated studying the literature of ancient Greece and Rome, increasing personal piety, and changing the Catholic Church.

e. The Metropolitan Transportation Authority (MTA) operates most of the transit systems in the New York area, and many people believe the MTA. does a pretty good job.

61—Numbers

a. Alfred E. Newman was born on April 1, 1954.

b. Correct.

c. Uranium's melting point is 1,132 degrees C, and its boiling point is 3,818 degrees C.

d. For our arboretum cleaning day, 143 people came to work.

e. You'll find him at 18 Orchard Road, which is at the corner of Main Street.

Review 1
a. Mr. Richardson and Jeanette Richardson have agreed to host our holiday dinner.
b. Correct.
c. Because Ted touched the poison ivy, he got a rash.
d. The lion is an animal well designed for stalking, for chasing, and for overpowering its prey.
e. The elephant trumpeted in triumph when it defeated its opponent.

Review 2
a. After the mixture boils for five minutes, it cools in the test tube.
b. If people in the country went shopping for a new car tomorrow, would they generally buy or lease?
c. There's no joy in Mudville: Mighty Casey has struck out.
d. I got lost because I was unfamiliar with the neighborhood.
e. Correct.

61—Review 3
a. Everyone who came to the restaurant loved the fat orange cat that lived there.
b. "Queenie" was her name.
c. Correct.
d. Few people knew the real reason she was there.
e. It was to keep the mice away.

Review 4
a. On July 20, 1969, Neil Armstrong became the first person to walk on the moon.
b. "Brillig" is a nonsense word which was coined by Lewis Carroll.
c. Correct.
d. I followed the street as we were told to do; Jenny took a short cut through the park.
e. The Library of Congress, which was built in 1897, contains 327 miles of bookshelves.

Review 5
a. The motion won by eighty-six votes.
b. The bear walked back and forth all day long in its cage.
c. The nutritionist at our cafeteria is anti-vegetarian.
d. When Little Red Riding Hood comments on her grandmother's big teeth, the wolf (who is disguised as the grandmother) replies, "The better to eat you with!"
e. I read Shakespeare's *Hamlet* six times before I saw the play performed.